Note from the editor:

It is with great pleasure that I present *Party Animal*, a project which took over two years to put together, but was definitely worth it! All the wonderful writers in this book kindly gave up their free time to help me help animals in need. I would especially like to thank Daphne Mackle, Sarah Webb, Mary Malone, Tracy Culleton, Susanne O' Leary and Catherine Daly who also kindly helped me with the mammoth task of editing this compilation of animal-themed fiction and non fiction. Huge thanks also to Linda Martin who has done such wonderful work over the years to highlight the plight of our furry friends. Special thanks to illustrator James Coyle for the beautiful drawing of our cover cat! He can be contacted at 00353-860614774 or jamesrosscoyle@yahoo.ie.

Finally I would like to dedicate *Party Animal* to the memory of Roberta Gray, a very talented young writer and animal lover.

All of the profits from this book will be given to worth-while animal charities including:

ASH Animal Rescue www.ashanimalrescue.com
Drogheda Animal Rescue www.dar.ie
The Donkey Sanctuary, Ireland www.thedonkeysanctuary.ie
Longford SPCA www.ispca.ie

Mid-Antrim Animal Sanctuary www.midantrimanimalsanctuary.org

Irish Guide Dogs for the Blind www.guidedogs.ie

Contents:

Foreword

Dear Reader,

I LOVE ANIMALS!

Well actually that's the understatement of the century. I can confirm unreservedly that 18 dogs and 4 cats share my house in the country, a house which over the last fifteen years, has welcomed animals of various shapes & sizes. I have homed everything from a Yorkie called Stanley, to an enormous German Shepherd called Basil. A couple of the dogs hobble on 3 legs, one is minus an eye, one is blind & deaf and two will never trust a human again. However all of them share one thing in common. They've all suffered varying degrees of cruelty and abuse at the hands of those who like to call them "their best friend".

As all animal lovers will tell you, there's no explanation for this profound love. I know as a little girl, I cared very little for the dolls and prams that were so beloved of my sister. Instead I was always to be found beside a wagging tail.

These days animals are part of our social and family life. They are masters at giving a shy child confidence or a senior citizen companionship. Not all of us have a large family circle! The love they give us is unconditional & priceless.

I work with many animal welfare societies. They're run

by unsung heroes – men and women surviving on a pittance, and always relying on donations from the public. Donations, by the way, include old blankets, towels & duvets. These keep the animals warm in winter and every donation is appreciated.

Isn't it wonderful that Marisa is donating the profits from this book to animal charities? Among them is Ash Rescue in Wicklow. Helena & Remy, who run the sanctuary, have dedicated their lives to saving animals. Spare cash for them is non-existent, what with food & vets bills for the 145 dogs that are currently looking for new homes. That figure doesn't even include the cats, horses, goats & pigs! Lots of the smaller animals share their house. However this house at the moment has a very large gap in the roof. Trust me when I say the tarpaulin which covers the gap is not waterproof. Leaving is not an option however.

TV3 has always been a stalwart supporter of animal welfare. Ash Rescue regularly appear on Ireland AM, surrounded by animals looking for new homes. TV3's support is immeasurable and through video footage, the public can see for themselves the conditions Helena & Remy work in.

So on behalf of those who can't speak for themselves, may I finally thank the authors who have given their words & time completely free. Heartfelt thanks for taking time out of your hectic schedules to contribute to this book.

Love & Whiskers,
Linda Martin

Mary Stanley's books include
*Retreat, Missing, Revenge, Searching
for Home* and *The Lost Garden*.

www.marystanley.com

1. RITES OF PASSAGE
Mary Stanley

When I was a little girl my outer world was wonderful. I lived with the sound of the sea from my bedroom window and a view across Dublin bay. In the gardens, blackbirds sang and a robin came through our conservatory window, through a broken pane of glass that was never repaired so that he would always have immediate access to the crumbs and seeds left out for him. They were halcyon days as my brother and I cycled around and around our garden on our little three-wheel bicycles.

We could tell the seasons, not just by the light or the heat, but also by the sound of the waves and the height of the tides. This world, the only one I knew, was magical. Of course there were other places we visited – the Japanese Gardens, the zoo and my grandparents' house to name but a few, but all the joy and fulfilment I felt was connected with the sea. And then, while I was still a little girl, we moved.

The move brought with it expectation and excitement, but at night I could no longer hear the waves crashing on the rocks, nor could I smell the salt in the air and perhaps it was because of that loss, that absence, that I began to fill my inner world with things to compensate. My grandparents' house was now next door to ours, and while it was structurally the same with three storeys and multiple rooms, it was completely different in atmosphere and sound. Our rooms were filled with children's laughter, paint boxes and paper, toys and books. Theirs was more peaceful with thick red carpets on the stairs and even the light came through the windows in a different, and perhaps, a calmer way.

Our house held its own excitement, with folding doors and cubby holes to hide in or behind, but we accessed these mysteries one by one until there was no place in it that was not ours to understand and to enjoy. My grandparents' house, on the other hand, held, and still holds, an undercurrent of something untapped.

I passed it recently and, looking up at the top floor, I saw how the window frames have rotted and the chimney pots are crumbling, and then I remembered the secret life I forged there.

Once upon a time, a long time ago, there was a little girl. Small, polite but mischievous, she appeared to do what she was told, and in her grandparents' home she played on the floor, or read quietly. She gathered raspberries in the garden and climbed the apple tree but, when her grandparents were not looking, she began a slow and systematic search of their house.

The drawers in her grandmother's bedroom smelled of lavender collected from the garden, and the dressing table with its three winged mirrors reflected the silver backed hairbrushes and the glass pots of hairpins and pieces of jewellery. Her grandfather's bedroom had an austerity about it with enormous mahogany chests of drawers and wardrobes. On top of one of the chests lay a series of stiff and starched collars ready to be buttoned onto his shirts. Her grandfather had opened Ireland's first travelling lending library, bringing books to remote villages the length and breadth of the country; his study carried a thousand books and over the years she read them all. But it was the top of their house – the third storey – that held her enthralled.

Her grandparents had three sons and they had all emigrated, and these uncles carried with them the mysteries of 'abroad' – Holland, Canada and Africa. Snippets of details came the child's way and she wove these bits of information into a tapestry of her own. This tapestry was comprised of words and the special meaning that the child gave to them – Inuit, clog, oasis, tundra, canal, desert . . . on and on went the list. Wonderful words with a flood of imagined images connecting them to each other. But one word stood alone – and that word was 'zebra'.

The word 'zebra' did not require her imagination, because she knew exactly what it was and where it was. Up there on the third storey of their house resided a zebra skin. It lay on the floor in an otherwise bare room, and when, on silent feet she ascended the stairs to explore, she found it in all its isolated glory on the wooden floorboards. She knew what it was. She knew that one of these uncles had shot it and sent the skin home to his parents as a gift. At first, she surveyed it tentatively, and later she brought a comb and smoothed it out. She tried to change the way the fur lay, but it was stalwart and would not vary its direction. Bit by bit, with increasing courage, she picked it up and held it.

The light came through the window and a sunbeam danced on the striped skin and she imagined an African horizon and the beating of drums. She began to dance with the skin in her arms, and later with the skin over her head. Her heels pounded on the floorboards, safe in the knowledge that her elderly grandparents were several floors below, out of sight and out of sound. She and Zeb, as she called this zebra skin, bonded as the drums beat louder and louder. They twirled among mud huts with straw roofs and she was clothed in a leopard skin with beads and bangles around her wrists and ankles. Zeb danced in unison with her, a dance that only an imaginary zebra could enact, rising beautifully on his hind legs like a Lipizzaner stallion. Around them dark hands beat rhythmically on the drums.

Her mother was a lover of theatre and ballet, and, as the little girl accessed new ideas and new music, she and Zeb entered into even more unlikely and exotic worlds. The Dance of the Sugar Plum Fairy had them both up on their toes and smiling at each other as they took to the boards in their imaginary theatre. In Swan Lake, they varied roles as Odile, Odette and Siegfried. They abandoned Siegfried in due course, and the child choreographed a new duet. Now she and Zeb took on the guise of the black swans and they danced together until they died in a cascade of feathers, which were in fact Zeb's hairs beginning to fall out in tiny showers of black and white.

She became concerned that he might fall apart. The stiffness of his skin had softened, and the stubbornness and roughness of his hair seemed altered. The idea of having to explain away his disintegration worried her.

But then, she found that she could still dance with him while he lay on the floor because his spirit had long since soared from the skin and was now a part of her. And such a part of her had he become, that she now had him with her when she left the upper floor. No one else could see him, but he was there with his strong intelligent face and his smooth striped body behind her at the dining table. Zeb went to school with her, nuzzling her hand or her shoulder when she was frightened or alone. He guarded her bedroom door at night, and little by little she stopped visiting her grandparents' top floor room. Zeb, who had once roamed the plains of East Africa, now lived an alternative lifestyle in Dublin 4. And instead of the sound of the sea haunting her sleep, the little girl heard the clippety clop of a zebra's hooves on the Masai Mara.

Her grandfather's bookshelves produced a book on animals giving her insight into the normal activities and the struggle for survival of a zebra in its native habitat. She read this with her customary curiosity even though she believed it had little relevance for either her or Zeb. But the facts were interesting. The female carries the young for over a year. Within an hour of birth the young can run fast enough to keep up with the herd. The herd can run at a speed of up to forty miles per hour. The stripes offer the zebra a strange sort of camouflage because, when they run, a predator has difficulty in discerning the individual, and so the mass of a herd makes each seem larger and blurrier than it actually is. She digested all of this.

A trip to the zoo saw her standing by the zebras' enclosure, watching a herd of them running together with a distinct lack of individuality. It was impossible to relate her zebra skin and the spirit that had emerged from it, with the mindless activity she was seeing before her. In the next enclosure the giraffes ignored her as they chewed leaves and towered above their captive world. Were they keeping an eye on the zebras? Her book said that giraffes often warn zebras about approaching danger. Perhaps in the elephant's eyes she saw something, some realisation of another world where captured animals should really be. She was allowed to feed bread to the elephant, the tip of his trunk curling around it as it lay flat on her hand, and she could feel the hairs on the end of it as they removed the chunk of food. She began to feel a terrible sense of sadness.

Back to the zebras she went. She wanted something more from them, but could not work out what it was. Her book had said that they live an average of ten years in the wild, whereas in captivity they could reach thirty-five. Which was better? Ten years of freedom or more than three times that, living in an enclosure behind bars and wire?

Watching them, she became disturbed by the knowledge that her Zeb had once run free. The idea that an uncle had shot him and that he must have fallen to the ground in a cloud of dust and blood distressed her. She could hear the pounding of his heart as he ran for his life, and then the shot – a single shot? – that brought him down. And for what? To satisfy the power of an individual human being? To prove that someone's aim was good? For sport? For his skin to be sent to someone's relatives as proof that they were thought of in a place where the sun was hot and water was lacking?

The inner world took on shadows. Clouds of uncertainty filled her skies. Slowly the magic diminished and her innocence ebbed. The little girl stopped dancing. She put away her book on animals and she grew up.

Alison Norrington's books include *Class Act, Look Before You Leap* and *Three Of A Kind.*

www.alisonnorrington.com

2. THE LOVE BIRDS
Alison Norrington

'There are hundreds of "better" birds. The colourful and elegant flamingo with its coral feathers and long, angular legs; the elegant swan with its S-bend neck; the colourful, mimicking parrot who can repeat what his owner says when nobody is listening and the cute picture-book robin with its plumped and ruby chest. And then there are the celebrity birds – Tweetie-Pie – infallible, cute and wry; penguins who even have a brand name and a chocolate bar named after them, right down to the irritating and hideously green Orville. But none of them are as lucky as me – Henry.

I'm a plain, virtually non-descript, blue budgie, but I belong. I've travelled with Emer all the way from Cork to Barcelona and my beady, black peppercorn eyes see everything.

I know I belong . . . .'

Henry had belonged to Emer for three years and had initially been worried when she'd got the job in Barcelona. He'd hopped and squeaked in protestation every time he heard her chatting to her mum in the kitchen about this wonderful chance to improve her knowledge of architecture, but he needn't have worried. She had taken him with her after all.

He'd been with Emer long enough to realise one strange-but-true fact about her – that sometimes she would wake up not knowing who she was with. Other times she would wake up not knowing where she was. But that morning Emer woke not knowing who she was or even what country she was in.

He suspected, by her groggy groans, that she wasn't quite sure whether it was nirvana, nausea or nostalgia, but he was watching her as she flickered her brown eyes open. She relied on him – he knew she did. He hopped across from perch to perch, inadvertently banging his small head on the irritating jingly-bell mirror as he did so.

He chirruped, noticing the numbers on her alarm clock had clicked past eight and that she'd be late for work again. That would make it nearly every day this month that she had been late! Ever since Ben had left really . . .

Henry wasn't really sure whether her change in behaviour actually coincided with Ben going, but he knew she wasn't coping too well lately. Since Ben had gone from Emer's life she had really taken a nose-dive. She used to spring out of bed and do some weird yoga poses and throw some unusual shapes and hum, nearly always on top form. Nothing like she was now. Henry knew she relied on him.

Emer lay still in her bed and Henry listened to the muffled sounds filtering through the closed shutters as Barcelona buzzed and hummed its way to life on this spring morning. Henry checked the clock numbers again – 8:10 am

Any minute now he suspected, Emer would roll over, groan and go back to sleep and be late again. He chirruped again, hopping across from perch to perch excitedly, deliberately clattering against his water dish and then knocking into his seed tray, scattering seeds from a height down onto the white-stained floorboards.

"Jesus Henry! Give it a break will you?"

She was awake. He chirruped again, proud of himself. She relied on him – he knew she did.

The start of another day and Henry had done his job. He watched Emer as she lay starfish in her bed, the light cotton sheet crumpled around her feet. She took a deep breath and glanced upwards, around the sage green room, the sunlight striping her bed with yellow lines, the robust tulips crying out from the glass vase, desperate for some light.

Henry watched as she stumbled from her bed, paused at the mirror to grouch and moan at her reflection, criticising her 'mousy' blonde hair and flat chest. But he thought she looked great. He loved her. He sat patiently waiting while she went into the bathroom and he looked forward to her re-emerging. She somehow changed when she was in that room, into someone more caring and kind. Someone more like the 'old' Emer.

Emer had been fanatical about Barcelona for years. She'd been halfway through her architectural studies when Barcelona had indulged itself in more self-promotion, coining 2002 the International Year of Gaudí. She adored the master-piece genius of Gaudí and had written much of her dissertation about him and his architecture – the impressive Sagrada Família that he had begun to design way back in 1883 and the fabulous La Pedrera.

Now she was working as a junior architect in the Eixample area of the city. And things had been great – until she had met Ben. The sex-on-legs street performer who had caught both her eye and her heart last year in the lush green Parc

Ciutadella when he, sprayed from head to toe in gold, had shimmered beneath the sunlight and had jerked from his statue-like pose, causing her heart to both stop and start at exactly the same time. Shame he had then gone on to break it in half . . .

The bathroom door clicked open and Emer appeared, lips painted, hair glossy. She crossed the room, turning on her favourite R&B music, and humming to the soulful tunes as she pulled on her underwear. Henry loved this time of the day, although her choice in R&B had rather taken a nose-dive too. Where she once listened to the funky and melodic songs, she was now favouring the painful and heart-breaking ones.

He looked across at her strangely sun-tanned body – a photographic negative of when she was clothed. Emer didn't much get the chance to sunbathe and so she was lightly tanned down her arms and across her chest, with the imprint of her spaghetti-strap vest stamped in white onto her skin. She remained white all the way down to mid-thigh, where she was sun-kissed all the way to her toes.

Henry was slightly envious of Emer – he would have loved to feel the sunshine directly on his feathers – just for a few minutes every day. As she pulled on the sleek trouser suit and vest top which were waiting patiently on a wire hanger Henry felt guilty for his jealousy. Emer loved him – she needed him, and he chided himself for wishing for any other life than the one she gave him. As always she gathered up her things into her small bag, came over to Henry's small cage, and stuck her finger in, wiggling and saying, 'Morning Henry. Bye Henry.'

His eyes sparkled like two glimmering drops of hot tar as he squeaked, slightly aggrieved that she hadn't bothered to refill his seed tray or to replenish the water that he had deliberately spilled earlier. He wasn't going to complain though. After all, she had had a lot on her mind lately and she was relying on him. He knew she was.

Gomez crouched behind a bush on the outskirts of Barcelona Zoo. It was one in the morning and he was waiting to spray little pictures – his signature – on the rockery and walls of the zoo. He was well known in Barcelona and had a massive following of appreciative fans. Gomez insisted that he was an artist – a grafitti artist, true, but an artist nonetheless. The park in which the zoo was housed was well protected – brightly lit and peppered with cameras and armed Guardia Civil in jeeps. It was beside the Catalan parliament.

As he crept lightly through the dense shrubbery at the edge of the park a patrol car drove by. He froze. The jeep stopped. His heart banging in his muscled chest he tried desperately to breathe quietly. A count of ten, and he heard the rumble as it drove off again into the night. Hoisting his rucksack onto his back he felt the thud against his spine as the ten spray cans inside slammed against him. He tried to look through the fence but found it difficult to see anything as it was so thickly covered in ivy. He hadn't anticipated the demented, crazy sounds of the zoo at night – sounds like babies crying and frenzied animals trying to rattle the cage doors off their hinges.

Quickly checking around him Gomez threw his rope up and over the high fence and swiftly launched himself over, into the zoo. He made his way to the penguin area. He sprang over the low wall and jumped the small moat and was soon squatting on the boulders and stones, littered with fish bones, as he sprayed his trademark 'quip' onto the huge rock. 'P-p-p-piss off' was soon artistically and very colourfully providing a backdrop to the penguins' enclosure. Within half an hour he had hot-footed it across to the giraffes' area and, crouching beside a huge pile of dung, had sprayed in Spanish – 'It's bloody freezing up here!'

Henry spent every day alone and was used to it. Lately though, he seemed to spend most of the morning worrying about Emer. He knew that she believed in love at first sight, and he worried that it made her vulnerable. But this was something else – she had been out at work all day and still wasn't home! It had got dark hours ago and Henry looked at her clock as it lit up the room with 1:50am. He was terribly anxious. He had spent the hours between seven and nine cheeping and hopping, waiting for her to come home. Then he had become a little quieter from nine to eleven – half expecting her any minute. But from eleven o'clock onwards he had barely moved, beside himself with worry.

It wasn't unusual for Emer to go out. She had a lot of friends in Barcelona and socialised quite a lot, but not on week nights. Never on week nights. He knew that she missed her friends from home, and that they were envious of her working (and partying) in Barcelona. So it was good for her to go out. But not this late.

Emer used to laugh as she'd talk to Henry about her jealous friends from home, saying, "They don't know the half of it! It's obvious that they've never tried to open a Spanish bank account, get a non-smoking table in Barcelona or try to park a car in the city centre, but hey, we'll let them have their fantasy, eh Henry?"

Gomez had made his way back through the Old City, through the Raval and La Ribera areas, finally stopping at an all-night café for a much-needed bottle of beer. He knew it must be just after two in the morning as Bar Manolo was emptying out onto the street.

Just then Emer burst onto the busy pavement, joining in the chant of 'Perqué?' as she and her co-workers conga'd and sang to their colleague Maria, asking her why she wanted to leave her office job for something more exciting! They conga'd into the café in which Gomez was enjoying his beer. Emer accidently stumbled and kicked his large rucksack over. Numerous cans of spray paint rolled out.

"Jesus! What have you been at?" she asked him.

"Nada."

"Nothing?" she repeated, grinning at him even though she found it difficult to focus. She pulled out a chair and sat down beside him. "Come on. You have a guilty look about you."

"Not at all," he spoke with a delicious gravelly voice and Emer's tummy flipped. His smile revealed a near-perfect set of pearly white teeth and she was hooked. This was it. Love at first sight. Well, maybe blurred sight, but she wasn't in a fit state to start splitting hairs.

A month later Henry was equally as angry with Emer as he had been on that hideously late night – he'd lost feathers worrying about her and still hadn't recovered. She'd finally rolled in at dawn break, towing some Spanish, shaven-headed yob with her. He had pretended to be asleep on his perch when she had called in sick to work the following morning, and had unashamedly listened to their conversation.

Gomez's English was pitifully cockney and Henry imagined that he had learned most of it from watching *EastEnders*, especially as he insisted on calling Emer 'Babe'.

His mistress had challenged Gomez about his graffiti and Henry had wanted to flap and fly and punch the air with delight when she got angry with him about defacing the beautiful city of Barcelona. Disgruntled though, Henry had listened as Gomez had defended his actions.

"No Babe, let me explain to you. Vandals are twisted people who deface our cities, leaving idiotic scribblings for all to see. They invade communities and make people feel dirty and used. They take, take, take Babe. You know who they are?"

Emer had shaken her head, wide-eyed. Gomez had held her hands in his tanned slender ones and had flashed his long eyelashes at her.

"They are called advertising agencies. They try to monopolise our thoughts, just like the television, they feed on our human inadequacies. So where is our freedom of speech? Imagine, Emer, a city where people could draw what they liked – perhaps even designated areas for free expression. A million colours at the bus stop would mean waiting would never be boring."

Emer threw back her head and laughed. It unnerved Henry. He hadn't seen her laugh like that for months.

"Gomez," she stroked his cheek with her hand, "you're a rebel. I don't agree with what you do, but I admire your passion."

Henry was on the verge of toppling from his perch.

And then Emer did it. She kissed Gomez. Hard and long. Henry felt sick. It was time to protest. If 'golden boy Gomez' was entitled to his freedom of speech, then so was Henry.

"Jesus Henry! What is it with you these days?"

Henry chirruped and continued to pretend to stare at his reflection in the grimy mirror that jingled from above. Emer squatted below his cage and wiped the floor with kitchen towel. Henry was trying not to smile. He hated to admit it, but he had become rather proud of the way he'd learned to cock his tail out from between two of the cage bars and poop from a height onto the floor. It was driving Emer positively mad, and he was loving it.

He had become deliberately clumsy too in the last few weeks. Since Gomez had appeared really, but he suspected that Emer hadn't twigged. He was now expert at bashing his seed tray and sending the entire contents crashing to the ground, and he could tip his water dish over with one swift flick of his tiny webbed foot. Emer was losing her patience with him.

However, sooner or later, she would realise that yes, Henry was actually quite getting to like Gomez. For all his bravado and shaved head and tribal tattoos, he really was a softie at heart. Henry watched how Emer would sidle up to him as they lay on her bed, watching the Disney videos that he was such a fan of. He adored animation and Henry had found it hard not to chirrup and cheep excitedly on the evening that he'd brought back *The Little Mermaid* – he adored the seagull from that film.

Henry had started off by keeping his back turned to the television when they were watching *Bambi*, *Lady and The Tramp* and *101 Dalmations*, but over time he had started to watch through the reflection on his mirror – *Finding Nemo*, and then by *The Lion King* he'd succumbed completely.

Now, as they watched *The Aristocats*, he made no secret of standing on his perch as close to the front of his cage to get the best possible view. Henry had begun to change his mind about Gomez – he wasn't so bad after all. If only his beloved Emer could remember him once in a while though . . .

It was early one evening when Gomez arrived with the small box. Henry felt sick. He knew they were mad about each other, but he hadn't expected this. Not so soon anyway.

"Emer, I have present for you," he had crooned from the doorstep.

Henry's heart flipped with fear as he heard Emer whimper, "Oh Gomez, you shouldn't have."

"Oh, yes I should. All good things come in small packages, Babe."

Henry couldn't look as Emer choked back her emotions, "Gomez, really. It's beautiful. I love it. The colours are fabulous. How could I possibly say no?"

Henry couldn't take any more. This was verging on the ridiculous – a proposal after only a few months! OK, so he was beginning to like the guy, but for Emer to marry him!

Henry turned his head, only to catch sight of them kissing, and then he started to cheep and chirrup like crazy, determined to put in the performance of his life as he went bananas inside the confines of his cage. The chrome cage rattled on its stand as he jumped from perch to perch, back and forth in a frenzy.

He knocked his seed tray and sent it flying, cracking as it hit the floor. He flicked his water dish until it splattered all over the sandpaper at the base of his cage, wetting himself and the floor.

There was no way he could allow Emer to do this. Love at first sight was one thing – but marriage? In his panic Henry didn't hear Gomez and Emer as they approached his cage smiling. Then he heard Emer's light, warm voice speaking gently, "Henry! Really, what a mess! What am I going to do with you? Your hormones must be raging eh? Look Henry. Look what Gomez has brought for us."

And with that Henry blushed as the most beautiful, jade green and yellow lady budgie was placed elegantly on the sodden, wet and incredibly messy sandpaper of his cage. She looked around horrified at the mess, and then looked up at him, at his puffed up chest feathers and glorious black all-seeing eyes.

Then Henry just knew he belonged!

Susanne O'Leary's books include
European Affairs, Diplomatic Incidents,
Finding Margo and *Fresh Powder*

www.susanne-oleary.com

3. TRUE LOVE
Susanne O'Leary

Some people are born to dogs, some achieve dogs. I had one thrust upon me.

'I'm sorry, darling but your house has been broken into. They kicked in the back door.'

The voice was abrupt and instantly recognisable. It was Yvonne, our neighbour and dear friend in Tipperary. 'I told you to get a dog,' she said. 'You can't live in the country without a dog.'

'But you know I can't have one right now,' I protested. 'I go back and forth to Brussels and you know I have other things on my mind.'

'I could keep it for you when you're not here,' Yvonne offered. 'And you seem to be here more than there these days in any case.'

'I'll call you back.' I turned to my husband Donncha, who had just walked into the room.

'That was Yvonne,' I said. 'The house has been broken into. Our lovely house.'

His face fell. 'What damage did they do?'

'I don't know. Yvonne said the back door had been kicked in and everything pulled out of the cupboards.'

'Oh God.' We were both silent while it all sank in. 'I

knew it might happen one day,' Donncha said, 'You can't leave a house unattended without expecting a break-in sometime. But it's horrible all the same, of course.'

'What are we going to do?'

He thought for a while. 'You have to go back to Ireland,' he said, 'and see what damage has been done, install an alarm . . .'

I nodded. 'And I want to get a dog.'

'A dog? You want to get a dog?'

'You make it sound like a small elephant.'

'You know nothing about dogs.'

'And you do?'

'Yes,' he said, looking smug. 'I had a dog once, you know.'

'No, I didn't, actually. I never knew you had a dog.'

'Well I did. A puppy. It was lovely but, well, he didn't stay very long.'

'What happened to it? Was it killed?'

'No, my mother got rid of it when it peed on the carpet. She gave it back to the farmer. It took me a long time to get over it. But, seriously, how are you going to manage a dog when you're not really settled anywhere?' He paused and looked thoughtfully at me. 'I see,' he said slowly. 'You really want to . . .'

'That's right,' I said, feeling a little apprehensive. 'I thought I'd kind of move in there and, well, come here now and then, instead of the other way around . . .'

There was a long silence. 'Well, I suppose,' he said after a while, 'it would be nicer for you there. I know you love it – that place has come to mean a lot to you.'

'It has. And, in any case, we don't see each other that often with your work and long hours and all that . . .' I ended lamely.

'You're right. Yes. I think it might be a good idea.'

'You do? Really?'

'Absolutely. I only have about a year left here anyway. And with direct flights from here to Shannon, I can come over often. Yes, you go,' he said, 'install an alarm . . .'

'. . . and get a dog?'

'I don't know about a dog . . .'

'But it would be lovely, you know. They're such great companions, Yvonne says. She should know – she has six of them. I know I wouldn't feel lonely if I had one.'

Donncha laughed. 'It's not as if it's going to talk to you. It's not going to discuss the weather or explain the ins and out of the European Union.'

'Exactly. The perfect companion,' I said and went to book my flight.

I went back to Tipperary, replaced the back door and installed an alarm.

'You should really have a dog,' the nice guard said when he called in to make sure I was all right and not too upset about the break-in (they do that in the country). 'A dog is the best deterrent there is; a big one that barks loudly.'

'What have you done about getting a dog?' Yvonne asked a few weeks later.

'Nothing,' I said, wondering how I was going to explain my apprehension. It seemed like I was taking on a baby, and the slogan 'a dog is not just for Christmas' kept going through my mind.

'Where am I going to get a big dog that barks loudly?' I asked Yvonne. 'Sounds a bit daunting. I'm not sure I want a dog, actually.'

'But we should try,' she said. 'Let's see if we can get an adult dog, one that has been abandoned. One that is house-trained and well behaved. And if, after a while, you feel you can't cope with it, I'll have it.'

'Well maybe . . .'

'I'll set it up, then.'

'I've just spoken to Mary in Dungarvan,' Yvonne announced the following evening, sounding as if she had been in touch with the queen. 'She has the perfect dog for you.'

'Who is Mary in Dungarvan? And how can she possibly know what's the perfect dog for me?'

'This one sounds lovely. It's a bitch called Sheba and she is about four years old. Mary said she would be ideal.'

'But, hold on a minute, I'm not sure about this. Maybe we should wait a little and think about it . . .'

'I'll pick you up at two,' Yvonne insisted.

The next morning, I rushed to the pet shop and bought: a big plastic dog-bed, a soft cushion, a big bag of dry dog cereal I had seen advertised on TV the night before, two cans of dog food (in case Sheba wouldn't like the dry stuff in the bag), two plastic bowls – one red (for food), one green (for water), a squeaky toy, a leather collar, a red nylon lead, a rubber bone and a copy of *The Dog Owner's Handbook*. I was ready for my new companion.

During the drive, Yvonne explained that Mary was a woman who took in stray dogs and, unlike a dog shelter, kept them until she found the perfect home for them.

'How many dogs has she got?' I asked.

'Oh, one or two.'

As soon as we arrived, I realised Yvonne had seriously underestimated the number. The little house was heaving with dogs. There must have been at least forty of them.

'She's in the kitchen,' Mary said as we waded through

the throng of dogs of all shapes and sizes, 'I'll let you get acquainted.'

With that, she opened the door, pushed us into the kitchen and slammed the door shut. And there she was, standing in the middle of the kitchen. She was black, the size of a border collie with a long tail that wagged furiously when she saw us. I shrank back as the dog rushed forward.

'She just wants to say hello,' Yvonne said as Sheba jumped up and licked my face. 'Come here, darling.'

The dog gave Yvonne the same enthusiastic treatment. Then Mary entered the kitchen and the dog hurled herself at her.

'Down, Sheba,' Mary said, pushing her back, which didn't seem to have the slightest effect. 'You'll have to work on this,' she added, holding Sheba in an arm lock that would have impressed a sumo wrestler. 'She gets a little excited when she meets new people.'

'Eh, how about having a look at something else?' Yvonne suggested, waving in the direction of the back yard, where yet more dogs were milling around.

'This is the one,' Mary said sternly. 'I have nothing else that would suit.'

'But,' Yvonne started, 'maybe a Labrador-type would be . . .'

'Sheba is part Lab,' Mary said. 'And part Border Collie and part Lurcher and maybe a little bit of Jack Russell as well.'

'Four dogs rolled into one? Seems like great value,' I joked, but when I was met with a frosty stare from Mary, I realised this was serious business.

'She is the best dog I have,' Mary said. 'You're very lucky to get her.'

Realising there was no point in arguing, we went out to the car. Yvonne opened the door and Sheba jumped in and sat on the back seat as if she belonged. We said goodbye to Mary and Yvonne started the engine. The dog began to whine.

'Just a little nervous,' Yvonne said. 'She'll be fine once we're rolling.'

As the car gathered speed, the dog's whine turned to a yelp, then a kind of screaming. She scrambled across the seats to try and get onto Yvonne's lap.

'Grab her!' Yvonne shouted, swerving dangerously. 'Hold her down between your legs!'

I did as I was told, taking hold of the collar and forcing the struggling dog down by my feet.

'What's the matter with her?' I shouted at Yvonne over the din.

'She is probably terrified of cars,' Yvonne shouted back. 'Maybe she was dumped on the side of the road or something.'

The one-hour drive seemed to take forever as I fought to prevent the frantic dog from hurling herself at Yvonne again. Sheba's screams and yelps were ear-splitting and I was beginning to have serious misgivings about the whole expedition.

But, as the car slowed down and we drove in through the gates of our house, she had calmed down enough to sit reasonably still and just give the occasional yelp. I stroked her black silky head and she looked back at me with mournful eyes.

'There, there,' I murmured, 'good girl.' Then Sheba suddenly made a different sound. I looked down.

'Oh no, she threw up! My shoes!'

'My handbag!' Yvonne yelled, braking suddenly in a

shower of gravel. I opened the door and Sheba shot out of the car and started to run around the front lawn, her nose to the ground like a furry black Hoover. Slightly shell-shocked, Yvonne and I looked at each other. 'Well my friend,' she sighed, 'we got her here in one piece.'

'Yes,' I said, looking at the mess on the floor, then at Sheba, who was standing by the front door, eager to go and inspect her new home. 'We did.'

'You must be so excited. Your very first dog.'

'And maybe my last,' I said, envisaging what would have happened had my husband been there.

'I'll have her if you can't cope,' Yvonne reminded me. 'This is just a trial.'

'Are you sure? You wouldn't mind taking her?'

'Of course not. She's such a beautiful dog. But give it a little time. You will probably end up loving her.'

'Maybe.'

We cleaned up the mess and I said goodbye to Yvonne, feeling just a little nervous as her taillights disappeared down the road.

Yvonne rang the following evening. 'How's everything?'

'Fine,' I replied a little shakily.

'Dog sleep all right?'

'Great,' I said, omitting the fact that I had been up every hour to check on the animal who had been sleeping peacefully on the soft cushion in her new bed.

'That's a relief. Did she eat?'

'Yes, once I mixed the dry stuff with the gooey stuff in the can and poured some cream on it.'

'Cream? She's having you on big time,' Yvonne laughed. 'How is she behaving otherwise?'

'She's a bit frantic,' I said. 'She jumps up on me every

time I speak to her. She won't leave my side for a second and even follows me into the loo.'

'Oh, she's just feeling a little insecure. Probably afraid she's going to be dumped again. She'll settle down once she starts trusting you.'

'You remember how you said you'd take her if I couldn't cope?'

'Of course, darling. But this is only the first day. Give her a chance. A week or so . . . no other problems?'

I was going to tell Yvonne that Sheba barked furiously every time she heard a doorbell (even if it was on television), that she had attacked the post when it fell onto the doormat and eaten a bank statement, a royalty cheque and a party invitation, but decided not to.

Sheba had also run away twice and the second time I found her in the farmyard down the road, having rolled in something that smelled so foul it took two shampoos and half a bottle of Eau de Cologne to get it out. But I didn't want to look like a wimp. After all, this was only the first day.

Donncha called few days later. 'How are you getting on with the dog?'

'Not too badly,' I said, still feeling annoyed over the previous night's incident. Sheba had stolen the steaks I had planned to cook for some friends and we ended up eating vegetarian.

'No problems then? You like her?'

'I took her for a walk by the river this morning,' I breezed on, avoiding the question. 'Yvonne and all her dogs came too. Sheba jumped straight into the river and swam around, even though the water must have been freezing. Yvonne said it's the Labrador in her that makes her love water. And the

Border Collie part wants to round us up all the time, it's very funny. And she runs like the wind. That's the Lurcher, apparently.'

'How many dogs have you got?'

'Only one,' I assured him, declining to tell him that Sheba had chewed through one of the seatbelts in the jeep during the short drive to Yvonne's. She's an excellent guard dog,' I added in a kind of sales pitch, more to myself than anyone else.

'That's great. She won't let any burglars into the house then.'

'Or the garden,' I said. 'Or the farm next door. She terrified the guy who came to deliver the timber you ordered. Had him backed up against a tree. I tried to tell him she only wanted to lick his face, but he didn't believe me. I had to pull her into the house before he agreed to unload his truck.'

'Poor man. What's that noise?'

'That's Sheba playing with her squeaky toy.'

'She sounds like a real character.'

'You have no idea.'

We said goodbye and I hung up. Sheba stopped playing with her toy.

'Good girl,' I said. She jumped up and licked my face, ripping my new cashmere sweater. I looked from my ruined sweater to the dog. She was just standing there wagging her tail and, suddenly feeling I had come to the end of the road, I picked up the phone again.

'I'm sorry, Yvonne,' I nearly sobbed, 'I can't cope with this dog.'

'Are you sure? I know she's been a little frantic, but maybe she'll settle down after a while . . .'

'I don't care, I can't take anymore,' I exclaimed. 'She's driving me crazy!'

'OK darling. Don't be upset. I'll take her.'

'You don't mind?' I asked. Sheba was lying by my feet, her head on her paws, looking at me with that mournful expression. I turned my back on her.

'Of course not,' Yvonne said. 'I'd love to have her, really.'

'When can I bring her down?'

'Well, I'm sorry, but you're going to have to cope until Monday morning. I'm going away for the weekend.'

'Fine,' I sighed. 'I'll try. Thanks.'

'See you Monday.'

Three more days, I thought. Three days of frantic barking, jumping and whining. I felt relieved however, as I thought of getting back to peace and quiet again, to life without a dog.

The rest of Friday was peaceful. Sheba lay in the sun in the back garden while I pottered around doing various chores. As these were the last few days, I was beginning to feel more positive towards her, the way one would about a weekend guest who was leaving shortly. I gave her the occasional pat and she wagged her tail without opening her eyes. Saturday was spent very much the same way, with Sheba sunning herself by the back door and me at the bottom of the garden, picking the last of the blackberries, feeling oddly at peace with the world and quite secure in the knowledge that Sheba was guarding the house. At least I didn't have to worry about having leaving the back door open. And the thought that I would give her to Yvonne on Monday was like a weight off my shoulders.

On Saturday night we watched a scary movie together. At least I watched and Sheba lay at my feet, whining softly, moving her paws from time to time, lost in her doggy dreams. The wind howled outside and branches knocked against the window but I felt quite cosy despite the scary film, knowing that if anyone tried to break in, Sheba would give them a hard time. On Sunday we enjoyed a long walk in the mountains and then went to bed early.

'Well, this is the last night, girl,' I said as I brought her to bed. 'Tomorrow night you'll be sleeping in Yvonne's with all the other dogs.'

She yawned and trampled around in the bed, before settling down on the cushion, closing her eyes.

'Good night then,' I said. Sheba opened one eye and glared at me as if to say, 'Hey! I'm trying to sleep here'. I tiptoed out of the room and closed the door softly behind me

I spent Monday morning preparing for her departure; putting her bed, cushion, toys and what was left of her food in the jeep. I picked up *The Dog Owners' Handbook* but put it down again, deciding Yvonne wouldn't really appreciate it. I brushed Sheba until her coat shone and put the leather collar on her.

'There,' I said, 'now you're ready for your new home.'

Sheba wagged her tail in agreement and I went into the kitchen to have a cup of coffee before we left. While I drank my coffee, Sheba sat as usual by my side. I looked at her, thinking that from now on, she wouldn't be here. It was a moment I had looked forward to all weekend. As though reading my thoughts, Sheba put a paw on my knee and our eyes met.

One minute later, I picked up the phone.

'Actually, Yvonne . . .'

Julie Parson's books include *Mary, Mary, I Saw You*, *Eager to Please*, *The Courtship Gift*, *The Guilty Heart* and *The Hourglass*

4. MY BOY OLIVER
Julie Parsons

He is surely one of the most beautiful cats I've ever seen. He's a deep, rich chocolate brown, in wintertime the colour of Black Forest gateau, and mottled with shades of milk chocolate in summer when his coat loses its thickness. He is tall rather than big, with a neat head and eyes that are the colour of green glass roughened by seawater. He walks with a swagger that says, "Hey, look at me aren't I a handsome devil?" His tail swings smoothly from side to side in his wake, like an oar behind a rowing boat. And when he is happy and at ease, he lies on his back with his front paws drawn up and pressed together like a circus sea lion's flippers. He is Oliver. And he is mine.

Oliver was the first, and so far the only male cat I have ever owned. I didn't mean to be exclusive. It just worked out that way. Cats were girls. They were cute and pretty and funny and wilful. They played and teased and purred and snuggled. Occasionally they would show their claws and bare their sharp white teeth. But it was a display, a show of feminine wiles. It wasn't for real. When they began to attract male attention, when they rolled over and showed their soft tummies and squirmed from side to side, little gurgles of desire burbling from their throats, I would take them to the vet. And put a stop to all that.

"Don't be cruel," my friends would say. "It's not fair. Let them have a litter. They'll be miserable if you don't."

But I didn't believe any of their anthropomorphic reasoning. Cats were cats. They didn't know anything about freedom of choice or options in life. An overnight stay in the vet solved the contraception problem forever. And they didn't seem to suffer. Sure they came home with a nasty shaved spot on their sides, and a neat row of black stitches. Sure they had to be cosseted and spoiled and given extra cuddles and helpings of Whiskas for a few days. But after that they were back to their old bouncy, independent selves. Shinning up the apple trees at double quick time, chasing and occasionally catching a hapless sparrow, and purring as loudly as ever as they curled onto my lap as I watched TV.

And then along came Oliver. We were introduced to him via his older half sister. Nellie was the black of the inside of a bag of coal. Small and slight and self contained, she screeched with irritation if she was picked up without due warning, her spine twitching and her torso going rigid with anger. She was the most ruthless hunter I'd ever had in the house. She brought home a rat one morning. It was too big for her to kill. She dumped it in the kitchen and sat back to watch. When my husband went to the sink to fill the kettle, the rat was waiting for him. He chased it across the counter top and finally trapped it in the bread bin, then dispatched it with a swift blow from the garden spade. Nellie's yellow eyes shone with satisfaction. She cleaned her paws and went for her morning nap.

We expected that Oliver would share her murderous instincts, her dislike for human company, her lack of interest in our lives. But Oliver was cut from a different cloth altogether. He was affectionate and needy. And ever so greedy.

"More, more, more," he would miaow, as he cleaned his plate and wound himself around my shins, butting my knees with his forehead until I gave in and doled him out another few spoons. And he wasn't the bravest out there in the jungle that is the back gardens of south county Dublin. The cat flap would slap open and slap closed as he shot inside from a close encounter with something very large and scary.

And that was before he too made his trip to the vet. I didn't have a second thought about it. After all, I had vivid memories of my mother dealing with a tom when we lived in New Zealand in the 1950s. She caught the cat and dumped it into a dustbin with a piece of cotton wool soaked in chloroform. A brick on the lid made sure he couldn't escape. And then when he was out for the count, a neighbour who was doctor made a couple of slits in the cat's testicular sac and out popped its testicles, like two small peas. I had no intention of getting my hands dirty like she did. This was the 21st century after all, and that's what vets were for. So just before Oliver's six-month birthday he made the trip to the surgery.

"Pick him up tomorrow, he'll be fine," the nurse said. And I did. But he wasn't fine. He was a very sad and miserable boy. I rammed the painkillers and the antibiotics down his throat and left him by the radiator to sleep it off. But somehow he knew, in a way that the girls didn't, that life had changed forever. When he stopped hurting he moped and sulked and slunk around the house looking hard done by. Eventually he made his way out into the garden. I watched him scramble up onto the wall. He didn't seem to have any of the usual spring in his step. It's just the operation, I thought. He's still sore. He'll get over it. In time.

And in time he did. Sort of. He ate and grew and slept. He spent hours staring into the middle distance. And in the evenings he cuddled up beside me on the sofa purring loudly. And then there were the days when he slept and didn't purr. And when I touched him he growled softly, shook my hand away, and his chocolate coat, usually so shiny and clean, looked dull and dirty.

"Puncture wounds on his neck. Torn claws on his back foot. He's been in a fight, poor boy," the vet ran his hands down his flanks. "Problem for neutered males. They can't fight the way the toms do. They have a hard time."

And the look on his face when Nellie came in after a long night. He would sniff her and back away. Then sniff her again. And miaow plaintively as I loaded his plate with cat food.

Four years ago we bought a house on Sherkin Island in West Cork. A beautiful place with a big garden and nothing but fields and beaches and wild headlands all around. We decided we'd take the cats with us when we went there for the summer. We got the usual warnings about how cats don't travel well. But these ones did. Into their boxes and into the car. Off with the car and onto the ferry to the island. They hated the journey. But we were sure they'd be happy once they got there. And Nellie was. Ten minutes after arrival she became an island cat. Sitting on the wall staring down into the hedgerow, her yellow eyes focused, her body tense. Every morning her yowl of triumph as she brought home mice, rats, shrews. Sometimes she would eat their heads and leave their bodies and a smear of blood and entrails on the floor. Sometimes she would eat them all, and leave nothing, cleaning off her paws with an expert lick of her tongue.

But Oliver couldn't cope. Under the duvet was his favourite place. His morning nap stretched into the afternoon, and on into the evening, one eye occasionally opening to see when dinner might be. And sometimes when I would wake in the middle of the night, I would see his silhouette as he sat on the windowsill staring out at the stars.

"I don't understand what's going on with him," I said one day to the local vet when I bumped into him at the ferry. "He doesn't seem to be interested in anything here. His sister loves it. She's in her element."

The vet looked me up and down.

"Is he neutered?" he asked.

"He is," I replied.

"Ah," he said, "that explains it. Neutered toms tend to introspection."

"Introspection? Is that it?"

"That's it," he replied. "That's it."

I watched Oliver with renewed interest that evening. I noticed the way he lifted his head, a puzzled expression on his handsome face, then laid it down carefully with a sigh. I noticed how he turned and stretched, then rolled over and curled himself into an even tighter ball. I noticed how he sat on the windowsill, the slit-like pupils of his dark green eyes widening and narrowing as clouds drifted across the face of the sun. So that was it. He was pondering the meaning of life. And so far he hadn't come up with a suitable explanation. An honourable pursuit, I thought. It put him up there with the great thinkers of the world. Socrates, Plato, Thomas Aquinas, Descartes, Locke, Wittgenstein, Einstein. And our Oliver. It suddenly all made sense.

Gemma English's novels include
Tangled Up In You, The Trouble With Boys,
and *Three Wishes*

5. THIS CAT'S STORY
Gemma English

My earliest memory is from when I was six weeks old. I was living in a house on the south side of Dublin city. My name was "The kitten" and I was very small and black.

There were four people living in the house and they were all pleasant and kind to me. My absolute favourite person of all was Molly. She was seven years old and let me sleep in her bedroom. Right up on her bed at night. She carried me around and let me bump my face with hers. We had a bond and I loved her. She smelt of milk and her hands were always warm.

One afternoon while Molly was in school and I was in her room sleeping on the floor, curled up in her nightdress, I heard a terrible commotion downstairs. The adults were laughing and shouting at once. I heard something smash onto the floor. I jumped out of my den to have a closer look, went down the stairs and followed the noise into the kitchen.

Suddenly I was face to face with a huge dog, all snapping teeth and slobber. I was horrified but after a moment I gathered myself, arched my back and hissed at him. I slapped at him too and I would have hit him only he moved swiftly away. I was shaking like a leaf but I'd scared him off and I felt I'd made my point. However I kept my back arched and my fur raised high for a little while, just to let him know I meant business.

"Oh my God, the kitten!" Molly's mother said and picked me up.

"What about it?" her father asked.

"We can't have a cat and a dog. We can't possibly have both!"

"I paid good money for that dog and we need a guard dog."

I had a quick look to see where the horrible dog had gone, but it wasn't in the kitchen.

"But Molly loves the kitten," the mother said, rubbing my back very roughly as she spoke.

"Yes, but we need a dog. She'll forget about the cat in a few days."

"I wish you'd told me you were getting a dog! I would never have got her the kitten if I'd known!"

"Well, I didn't know you were getting the kitten, did I? You never said it to me either!"

"But Molly was looking for a pet. Last month all she did was ask if she could get a pet. So I got the bloody kitten!"

"Well I got her the dog and we could all do with having a dog around here. I don't even like that cat," the father pointed straight at me.

How dare he point at me like that! Didn't he know it was rude to point?

"The kitten will have to go back to the home," Molly's father continued.

"We couldn't give her back after only a week."

"Yes we could. People do it all the time."

"We'll have to talk to Molly about it. We can't just give it back without saying anything to her."

"No, just bring it back. If she hears about it she'll only get upset."

I was confused. What were they talking about? What home? I was home already. They were obviously talking about somebody else. Then they put me out of the kitchen and shut the door.

I wandered into the sitting room. The dog was sniffing around at a teddy bear Molly had discarded on the floor. I walked in behind the sofa so he wouldn't notice me, and I found a nice sunny spot there and lay down. Before I knew it I was sound asleep. Nobody came looking for me and it was night time when I woke up again.

I went to find Molly but she had already gone to bed. The dog was on her bed, in my spot! Molly's arm lay across his thick neck and he was snoring. I stood there hardly able to believe my eyes, but Molly was fast asleep and I didn't really want to wake the dog, so I went back to the sofa and settled in for the night.

The next day Molly's mother was up and dressed really early. I watched her walk around the sitting room looking behind the furniture and grumbling. She had a big box with her. She carried on searching for something and was also looking at her watch. She was obviously late so I decided to give her a hand. I called to her and asked what she was looking for.

"There you are!" she said and grabbed me.

All of a sudden I was in the box with the lid closed over. I panicked. What was this all about?

She looked in at me through a peep hole and then I realised we were obviously playing. I punched at her through the hole. I could just about fit my paw through. It was great fun, but Molly's mother didn't seem to enjoy the game half as much as I did. She stopped playing and so I sat in the box waiting. I waited and waited but she never looked in at me again.

Instead, when the box opened there was a different woman staring in at me. She was a young woman with lots of curly hair and she was very jolly, but a bit rough. She pulled me out of the box and checked my ears, then my mouth and then she grabbed my tail and looked at my bum. Molly's mother was talking in another part of the room. I kept my eye on her but then she walked out.

I shouted after her, she'd forgotten me. I didn't know where I was exactly and if she left me here I'd be lost. She never looked back once though. The door swung shut and I stared at it, willing it to open, but it never did.

I was taken down a long corridor with lots of rooms on either side. Every room held about four cats. They lay in bundles together, yawning and stretching. Where on earth was I?

Suddenly I was put in my own room, all alone. I walked all around and smelled everything – it all smelt funny. The woman gave me food and milk and a big rub. Then she shut the door and walked away. I called after her, but she never came back. I called and called until my voice was hoarse, but still no one came back.

Two days passed like this, with me all alone in my room. The young woman came and fed me and rubbed me down, but she didn't stay and she never played with me. Not like Molly.

Molly never came back either. I watched the door constantly but she never came.

Then one afternoon a man and a woman came in. They were laughing and pointing at the kittens opposite me. The other kittens purred, stretched and looked cute. One of them even rolled on the floor for them. They were very taken with her and rubbed her tummy.

I realised I had to do something fast to make them notice me. I stood in the middle of my room and I shouted at the top of my voice.

"Hey, look at me! Pick me!"

They didn't seem to hear me, but I just kept on shouting. Finally the woman came over and looked in at me.

"Look at this one. It's pretty, but I really didn't want another black cat," she said and moved on.

"Please pick me!" I shouted once more.

She came back and looked at me again, then the man came over and looked at me too. They opened my door and rubbed me down. I ran as fast as I could up the man's arm and on to his shoulder. He tried to pull me off, but I held on tight. They started laughing and rubbing me. The man stopped trying to get me off his shoulder, he just rubbed my head. It was working! They'd have to take me if I was stuck to their clothes, wouldn't they? What a good idea!

They asked the young woman about me and she said I was available to take away. She then came over and took me off the man's shoulder. She put me back in my room and to my anger, locked the door. The man and woman walked away. That young woman had blown all my chances. I'd been on to a winner and she'd ruined it on me!

A few minutes later the couple came back and looked in at me curiously, and finally that young woman reappeared. She opened my door and the other woman took me in her arms. They put me into a new box and into a car.

We drove for miles, perhaps even to another country. It took hours. Finally the car stopped and they brought me into a house. They put my box on the kitchen floor and opened the lid. I sat for a while looking at them. The whole place smelt new.

I stuck my nose in the air and sniffed, but I couldn't smell any other animals around. No dogs anyway, which was good. I got out of the box and walked around the room. They put out food and milk for me and stood back. They watched me while I looked all around the sitting room, dining room and kitchen. I checked everything, it all seemed perfect. I took a little drink and used my kitty litter. The woman carried me into the sitting room and sat me on her knee. She stared at me for ages, looking straight into my face.

"I think I'll call it Harvey," she finally announced.

"Harvey? But it's a girl," the man said.

"I don't care, I like Harvey."

"Alright, your choice."

So my name was changed from "The Kitten" to Harvey. They gave me a red collar and put a small door in the kitchen door especially for me to use. I use it all the time, it's so handy. My new adopted parents delight in my every move and talk about me all the time. They think I'm beautiful. I know because they tell me every day. And the best bit of all is I'm the only one. They have no other pets, no dogs. One particular dog visits from time to time, but he's smelly and pushy. He knows nothing about social space and invades mine all the time. Once he even sniffed my behind, but it was the only time he ever got that familiar I can tell you. He was slapped good and hard that day. Anyway, he never sticks around too long.

I have a great set up here. I'm a very important member of this family and I intend to keep it that way. It means a lot of hard work, but it's worth it. I walk around my garden and some adjoining gardens making sure that no new kittens try to move in. I have had to scare a number of them away. They can see very clearly that this is a great set up and they try to muscle in. I have to be on my guard all the time, if I let my defences down they might get a new cat or even a dog and I'd be put back in that room again.

I'm almost six years old now and I like it here. I'm used to it. I really don't think I'd be able to "sell" myself again and God forbid I should ever have to climb up on a shoulder. These days I get a bit nervous, I don't really have such a head for heights. Anyway, I'm happy here and they seem happy for me to stay.

I got a bit of a fright last July when the woman went away for a few days and came home with a baby. I really thought I was done for, but they just made me stay away from the cot. That was no problem because the baby smelt funny if you ask me. I didn't much like him at first. Now he's almost a year old and he seems to have grown into his head. He dribbles a lot and his hands are sort of sticky, but I think he's cute if a bit clumsy. He can't even walk, never mind run yet. And they still have to feed him. Imagine, he's nearly one year old and he's still being spoon fed! I don't understand it, but it doesn't really matter.

As I said, I'm happy here. They love me and treat me like a little princess. I still keep a careful eye on all visitors and I patrol the perimeters every day for at least an hour. Above all, I have to make sure I keep all other furry animals out. Believe me, I learned that rule the hard way.

Suzanne Higgins' books include *The Power of a Woman, The Woman He Loves* and *The Will to Win.*

www.suzannehiggins.com

6. HOGAN
Suzanne Higgins

This story is dedicated to Hogan Higgins – a truly marvellous dog and a wonderful addition to our family. Thanks to Celtic Animal Life Line for bringing us together . . .

Jenny started the week as she did almost every week. She rose at 6:30 am, threw a scrunchie in her hair and got into the tracksuit that she had picked out the night before. While her three children and husband slept soundly, she set the table for breakfast and made the school lunches. She emptied the dishwasher and the washing machine. Sometimes, if the weather was good, she hung the clothes outside, and if it was raining they were hung in the dining room. Today the sun was shining and it cheered her to get the shirts and smalls out into the fresh air so early. By 7:00 am the washing machine was reloaded and running again, and the kitchen was ready for the onslaught of her two big boys.

She cast a professional glance around her country-style kitchen. Two lunch boxes were perched on the sideboard, fully loaded and ready for collection. The baby bottles were lined up, full of freshly boiled water that would cool while she was out. The table was set and ready for action. Yes, she thought with satisfaction, she was ahead of the game. She double-checked the large chrome clock over the kitchen door although she knew exactly what time it would be. She knew she could be up and organised in thirty minutes flat because this had been her routine for the last twelve months. It had become an essential part of her life – her very existence.

Jenny rose so ridiculously early every day so she could have just one half hour – thirty sacred minutes – to herself each morning. Admittedly her two boys were at school for a great part of the day but little Jemima, her rather demanding one and a half year old, was still at home. This meant that between the older ones staying up late at night and her youngest being with her all day, Jenny had absolutely no time in her life that she could call her own.

It was John, her rather unsympathetic husband, who had, one day jokingly suggested that she get up earlier if she wanted time to herself. Jenny decided to do just that.

With everybody in the house still safely in the land-of-nod, all she had to do was glance in Hogan's direction and he was immediately by her side. The family dog was well used to Jenny's routine at this stage, and he knew not to crowd her when she descended upon the kitchen every morning. Hogan had learned to give her space while she whizzed around him and did her chores. Then, when all was done, they'd both set off on a thirty minute walk.

Ironically, while she desperately wanted a little time-out from her family, Jenny was more than happy to spend her sacred private time with the family dog.

Spring was in the air and within seconds Jenny was in good form. As she lengthened her stride and began to power-walk, Hogan shifted effortlessly from a walk into a gentle trot. A year earlier it had been a very different story. Neither had been particularly fit – Jenny because she had a relatively young baby and Hogan because he had sat around and eaten like a horse for the previous six years. However, now they were both considerably fitter and slimmer, they could cover three kilometres in thirty minutes with relative ease.

Hogan had been acquired when the Dohertys moved to Kildare some seven years earlier. Originally Jenny had fought the idea of a dog tooth and nail. The last thing that she needed was another four feet to clean up after. However, John had insisted.

"Every family living in the country should have a dog," he had enthused. Eventually with her sons and husband incessantly badgering her, she had given in and Hogan arrived in due course.

The Animal Rescue agency interviewed the Dohertys and in a matter of weeks they had an adorable little dog. He had been deserted on the side of the road although he was as cute as a button. Hogan still had his puppy features and the vet reckoned that he was about seven months old. What nobody could have guessed however was the size that 'cute little Hogan' would grow to. Perhaps that was the reason he had been deserted, Jenny mused as they burned along the country road together. Hogan could now easily pass for a small horse.

As the years passed, the vet had to review his original guess at Hogan's parentage. When he first saw him, he had reckoned that the dog was a Retriever-Collie cross breed. After a few years however, he concluded that Hogan definitely had some Irish Wolfhound in his blood! Whatever his mix though, Hogan was now very much part of the family and Jenny couldn't imagine life without him.

Kildare was a quiet, picturesque town and the Dohertys lived in a beautiful old country house with a tree-lined drive just half a mile outside it. Jenny was at last beginning to settle there. It had been a difficult move for a city girl but with time she had made some good friends and her two sons had little memory of living in Dublin. They were fiercely loyal to Kildare town and spent every waking moment in their local football club.

The walk Jenny took every morning was the same. It was a large circle which she found very satisfying as she didn't have to turn around and retrace her steps at any point. As yet another spring whispered gently over the beautiful countryside, Jenny realised that she really had become a Kildare woman. She no longer wanted to move back to Dublin. The realisation made her smile. John had spent all his time trying to convince her that country living was infinitely preferable to city life. He was originally from the midlands and so he was predisposed to living in a smaller town. Jenny, however, had always argued in favour of the big smoke. For this reason he regularly came home with large bunches of flowers or perhaps punnets of fresh strawberries when he passed a stall on the side of the road.

"These are for my city chick," he would tease her with a kiss on the cheek. "For putting up with country life," he explained as he gave her the little tokens of love.

Now as she walked along the country road she realised with a sudden start that she really had made the switch. She would hate to return to the congestion and smog of the city. Twenty-four hour shopping was vastly overrated.

"My God, Hogan, I really have become a country woman," she laughed. The dog looked up at her for a brief moment as if to say he had known that for some time.

"We can't tell John though. I might stop getting all those lovely goodies he bribes me with," she reasoned. "This has to be our little secret, OK Hogan?"

The dog barked in agreement. Then they turned the last corner and headed for home. The hound bounded forward to run the last stretch towards the house. With the fresh air in her lungs and the wind in her hair, Jenny was ready to face another day of sticky fingers, muddy football boots and dirty laundry.

Hogan reached the house first and didn't wait for Jenny. The dog flap, which he could still just about fit through, was unlocked so he barged straight through and up the stairs. The first room he hit was JJ's. Johnny junior was still sound asleep but opened his eyes when the dog made his now habitual leap onto the bed.

The ten-year-old squealed with glee and playfully wrestled with the hound for a few minutes before Hogan jumped off the bed and trotted in next door. Robert, at the ripe old age of fourteen, was not so easily woken. Hogan had learned this the hard way. He knew not to jump up on the bed – not unless he wanted a good belt. Instead he stood next to Robert's pillow and gently nuzzled the quilt. Robert groaned audibly but rewarded Hogan's wake-up call with a clumsy scratch behind the ear. Satisfied that he was more or less awake, the dog wandered out of the room to see if Jenny had caught up with him yet.

At fourteen years of age, however Robert had other things on his mind, like Trinny Williams. Trinny had moved to Kildare the previous spring but hadn't noticed Robert until Christmas. At a New Year's disco Robert's best friend, Michael Fagan had introduced them. That was as far as their relationship had progressed, but in Robert's imagination it had gone so much further. In his dreams, Trinny was his girl. She let him hold her hand in public and he got to kiss those incredible lips . . . but just as things were getting interesting Hogan gently pushed the bedroom door open again.

"Get out," he growled at the poor dog.

Hogan responded with a plaintive cry.

"Sorry, dog," Robert rubbed the animal's head affectionately. "My mind was elsewhere."

The dog looked at him with his head at a slight tilt as if he was taking it all in. Robert smiled at him. "I was thinking of Trinny if you must know. She's some girl, Hogan. How the hell do I get her to like me?"

The dog barked and licked his lips as if he understood exactly what Robert was feeling. Despite the fact that he was only waking up, Robert laughed. "Let's keep this a secret Hogan, right?"

Jenny arrived upstairs just as the dog was exiting the boy's room.

"Everybody up?" she called to her boys. There was a collective response of groans. The day had begun in earnest.

With the boys now awake and starting to dress themselves, Jenny headed for the baby's room. She heard the pump of the pressure shower in her ensuite kick into action. No need to check on her husband. He was obviously up already.

Despite her desperate need for a little quiet time, Jenny's favourite time of the day was waking Jemima. As with all the others, Hogan was already in situ. Unlike with the boys however, he did not wake the baby. He didn't even go near her cot. Hogan just sat near the door and waited for Jenny to gently open the curtains and whisper to her youngest.

Within minutes the little girl was standing up in her cot

eager to be lifted out and chat with her mother. With a new nappy on, Jenny put her baby on the floor where Jemima made a bee line for her four-legged friend. Hogan lay down patiently showing no sign of aggression or impatience while Jemima clambered on top of him in her enthusiasm to say hello.

Eventually everyone descended into the kitchen. Cereals were poured, coffee was brewed and lunch boxes were stuffed into bulging school bags. Jenny reckoned that the nicest thing about living in Kildare was the lack of city traffic. The boys had their breakfast at around eight and could leave the house as late as a quarter to nine. It was only a ten minute walk into the town and their school. Another advantage was that the primary and the secondary schools were right next door so JJ had the company of his brother for the whole walk.

John was the first out the door. With just a mug of black coffee and a slice of toast, he grabbed his suit jacket and his briefcase and kissed his wife and daughter goodbye. His sons received a collective wave.

"Be good at school, boys," he added for good measure.

The Doherty family had moved to Kildare when John was offered the head of marketing position in Digisav – the computer parts giant. Although it was a huge company with factories worldwide, the company in Kildare was one of its larger ones. It gave employment to many people in the region and Digisav worldwide was going from strength to strength.

This morning, however, John was a little hungover. Himself and Jenny had shared a bottle of wine with their dinner the previous evening but when she had retired for the night, he had stayed up, poured himself a double whiskey and flopped down into the armchair in his study. Hogan had walked in and lay down beside his master's feet. John kicked off his shoes and scratched the dog's tummy. The dog was in seventh heaven as the man sat there worrying about his future.

While John loved his job and the company, he could be facing a problem shortly. He'd heard he might be in for a big promotion. He had done seven years in Kildare and the company's market share had increased tenfold in Ireland, but John knew that a promotion could only mean one thing – relocation. The head office for the European operations was in Dublin so at least they would still be in Ireland, but he really didn't want to leave Kildare. He loved the town, was very involved in the local tennis club, and the kids loved their schools. But there was Jenny to think of too. She made no secret of the fact that she missed Dublin desperately, not that he could see why. Hogan sensed John's unease and got up to rest his nose upon his master's lap.

"What will I do Hogy? If I tell Jenny about the promotion she will certainly want to move back to Dublin but I really want to stay here. What about you?"

Hogan licked John's hand. "You like it here don't you?" John took another gulp of whiskey. "And so do the kids. Perhaps I should hold off telling her just until I actually get the offer. Can we keep this between us just for the time being, Hogan?"

The dog continued to lick.

"Good, Mum's the word," John smiled as he rubbed the dog's head.

"OK, it's 8:45 am, time you two were gone," Jenny said trying to keep the boys moving as she glanced up at the clock in the kitchen. JJ was playing with his Weetabix however.

"Come on JJ, chop chop. Is something wrong? What's taking you so long?" his mother asked but her attention was more focused on Jemima's bread and jam not hitting the kitchen floor. He saw that she wasn't really looking at him and so he sank deeper into his silence.

Jenny got their coats and eventually got them out the door. It was only when she returned to the kitchen that she found Jemima gleefully throwing her jam and bread onto the floor – jam side down, of course. She called for the dog to eat it up but to her surprise he was nowhere around. This was quite unlike Hogan as he knew that meal time was the best time for leftovers. Jenny didn't worry unduly however. He would turn up eventually.

Every morning Robert walked his little brother to the gates of his school. "Good luck, JJ. See ya later," Robert tussled the younger boy's hair.

JJ was quieter than usual. He had something on his mind. Surely Conor Williams was only joking? It was a stupid joke if it was a joke. All too soon however, JJ had his answer.

"Well, did you bring me the money?" Conor appeared from nowhere.

JJ nearly jumped out of his skin. "Eh, hi Conor. Sorry what are you on about?"

The bigger boy came right up to JJ and bore down on him. "I told you to get me some money. Your dad is the bleedin' boss in that factory. Yeez are loaded. Did you get me the money?"

Conor Williams, although the same age as JJ was a good six inches taller and considerably broader. He had only moved to Kildare the previous year from Dublin, but had quickly acquired the reputation of a man not to be crossed.

"Jeez, Conor, my dad's not the boss of Digisav. I thought

you were only joking," said Johnny junior, trying to charm his way out of the situation. He could already feel the sweat on the back of his neck and on the palms of his hands.

Conor grabbed him by the scruff of the neck and pulled him behind the school hedge.

"What am I going to do with you, little man?" he snarled. "If I let you away with this, my rep is ruined. "You do understand where I'm coming from?"

JJ's fear turned to cold terror as he realised that none of his classmates were around to help him. He closed his eyes tight in preparation for the first dig. When he heard a deep guttural snarl he just assumed it was Conor. The noise was savage and primal. His enemy was a monster and JJ was terrified.

It was only when Conor let go of JJ's collar and he fell to the ground in a lump that he dared to open his eyes again.

"What the hell is that?" Conor screeched as a huge beast brandishing two inch canines crouched down in the pre-attack position just metres away. The animal's eyes were wide and angry. Saliva dripped from his half-open and snarling jaws.

"Hogan!" JJ had never been so glad to see his dog in all his life. "What are you doing here?"

He got to his feet, feeling considerably safer with his dog next to his side. On hearing JJ's friendly tone, Hogan stopped snarling, licked away his drool and trotted over to the little boy's side.

"Is everything OK?" Robert Doherty also appeared from nowhere.

The younger brother couldn't believe his luck. "Rob, what are you doing here?" But Robert recognised a near-miss when he saw one. Two fellas behind a bush, one tiny, one huge? JJ was definitely in trouble.

"Who are you?" Robert took an aggressive step towards the bully and JJ saw his opportunity.

"Easy, Robby," he spoke lightly to his brother. "This is just a friend of mine. His name is Conor and we simply had a small misunderstanding. Isn't that right Conor?"

The bully didn't like the look of the older brother but the psycho dog really freaked him.

"Yeah, that's right," he gulped. "All a big mistake," he echoed. "No harm done."

JJ was beginning to enjoy himself. "Conor Williams meet Robert Doherty. Robert meet Conor."

The two boys shook hands warily but in a flash Robert realised that he was talking to Trinny's little brother. "I think I know your sister to see," he said as the school bell began to ring.

"Yeah?" Conor didn't really care. He was just anxious to get away from the dog. "We better go, JJ. That's the bell. Nice to meet you, Robert. Bye."

He scampered off.

"What brought you back here?" JJ asked, never so relieved to see his big brother.

Robert gave him a rare brotherly hug and explained. "Hogan must have followed us to school. He was looking out for you, little bro. Just after I said goodbye to you he came up to me and began to bark like a crazy dog. Then he ran back here so I thought I'd better follow him."

"Really?" JJ was still on cloud nine after his near-miss. "Lassie eat your heart out!"

The boys laughed. "Look, is that guy giving you grief, JJ? If he is, we need to put a stop to it."

"I didn't want to tell anyone," the younger brother explained. "The only one I told was Hogan but I swore him to secrecy."

Robert smiled. "Well he didn't actually tell anyone now, did he? Look, if that little bugger gives you any more trouble you tell me. I'll have a word with him."

JJ knew exactly what kind of word Robert was talking about. Sometimes, just sometimes, it was really cool having a big brother.

"Actually, Rob I don't think he'll be giving me any more trouble, but I'll keep you in the picture."

Then the younger boy turned his attention to the dog. "And as for you?" he wrapped his arms around the animal's great big neck, "you're simply the best dog anybody could have!"

Robert watched JJ scamper into school as he stroked his dog's head. "Well, I think I've definitely blown any chance I had with Trinny now, Hogan. What do you think?" he whispered as he turned and headed for his school and Hogan headed for home.

The following weekend was the Digisav spring barbeque. John was acutely aware that he hadn't told his wife about the now imminent promotion. Until now it had only been a possibility so he'd decided not to bring it up. Just after lunch the previous day however, the MD of Digisav had cleared any tiny doubts, and John had been offered the Dublin-based position. He came home with a heavy heart, ready to tell Jenny. But when he got home he was greeted by the babysitter.

He'd completely forgotten that Jenny's book club was the first Friday of the month. This now meant he wouldn't have a chance to discuss the promotion with Jenny before the barbeque.

Of course it did come as a complete surprise when John's managing director came up to her at the toasted-buns-stand and congratulated her for being married to the Head of Marketing of Digisav, Ireland. She looked at him blankly as Jemima pulled her hair impatiently. John appeared by her side the minute he saw his boss talking with his wife.

"Darling," he smiled at her and he glanced at the MD, "can I have a word?"

He guided her away by the elbow. She looked at him quizzically. "It all happened so fast," he explained. "I just didn't get a chance to tell you."

"And what about this morning, John? Why didn't you tell me then?"

Jemima wriggled to be put down.

"You've been promoted?" Jenny continued with a look of utter bewilderment on her face. "Didn't you see it coming? What does this mean for us?"

She tried to digest the bombshell but then she grinned at her husband. "More money?"

He laughed, "Yes, but the biggest part of it is you get your wish. We'll have to move back to Dublin. That's where Head Office is."

"Dublin?" she whispered looking more than a little concerned.

He was surprised by her reaction. He had honestly expected a whoop of joy and a hug. But she looked into his eyes and took his hand.

"John, we have to talk. There's something I need to tell you."

Trinny Williams was surprised when a big shaggy retriever type dog walked up to her and began to lick her on the hand. She was equally surprised when a toddler ran up to him and began to pull out of his coat. If she didn't know better she could have sworn that the dog was minding the child.

Trinny bent down on her hunkers. "And who do you belong to, little angel?" she asked of the baby. Jemima made strange, however and so she began to wail. It was hardly surprising that Robert was first on the scene as he had had his eyes glued on Trinny all afternoon.

"Hi." He closed the gap between them in a matter of seconds. "That's my little sister – trying to escape again!" He grinned at the object of his heart's desire.

"Robert, isn't it?" Trinny smiled meekly as he scooped up his baby sister. The little girl stopped crying instantly.

"Yeah, but you can call me Robby."

"God, you're a natural with kids. I wonder if you could tame my thug of a little brother."

"Conor?"

"You know him, already?" she blinked and grinned causing Robert's heart to somersault.

"We've met. I think he's a friend of my kid brother's.

"Look, can I get you a coke or a burger?" he asked.

Trinny laughed. "You're the one holding the baby. Maybe I could get you one?" she offered.

He smiled inanely. As Trinny turned to walk towards the burger stand with them, Robert gave Hogan a quick wink. Was it really possible that his dog had engineered that little introduction?

"Good boy," Robert whispered. "You're my wonder-dog."

En route they passed JJ and Conor Williams. JJ had been enjoying a new heightened respect among his peers, as the story of how he beat Conor Williams into submission became the stuff of legend. Conor and he were now on an equal footing for all to see at the barbeque.

John bear-hugged his wife and laughed. "So you don't want to leave Kildare at all now? Not even for a considerable jump in salary and a move back to Dublin?"

Jenny beamed back at him and shook her head. "I don't want to leave Kildare."

"But I thought you were a city girl," he argued.

"I was, but now I'm a country girl," she explained.

"Why didn't you tell me that you had changed your mind about city life?"

"Well, I told Hogan but it was our little secret."

"That's funny. I told him about the possibility of my promotion but I swore him to secrecy too. So we're agreed, we're not taking the promotion, right?"

"Right," she hugged her husband.

John looked around him. "Where is the mutt anyway?"

"It's OK. I'm watching him," Jenny smiled. "He's been chaperoning Jemima around the barbeque for the last ten minutes. They're with Robert."

John whistled and the dog came bounding back at the sound of his master's call.

"Hogan, you're bloody good at keeping secrets." John Doherty patted his big dog's head and offered him a sausage.

Trinny, Robert and Jemima came up to the Doherty parents just as the huge succulent burgers were being handed out.

"Look who we found wandering around by herself with Hogan," Robert explained as he returned his baby sister to his mother's arms.

Jenny wasn't concerned about her little girl. Unbeknownst

to her eldest, Jemima had never been out of her mother's eyesight. It was just one of those things that a mother got used to doing. Now however, was not the time to tell Robert that. He seemed quite anxious to introduce his young lady to his parents.

Trinny seemed like a lovely girl, Jenny decided. She was absolutely sure that she wanted to stay in Kildare now. To hell with the pay rise. She loved county life and her early morning walks with her dog. Trinny petted the huge animal who sat happily in the middle of the group.

"Whose dog is he anyway?" she asked lightly.

John, Jenny, Robert and even little Jemima all looked at her and replied, "mine" simultaneously.

But JJ arrived back just in time to hear Trinny's question, and dismissed his family out of hand.

"Don't mind any of them Trinny. That dog is actually mine," he corrected. "I'm the one who feeds him and cleans his bed. He's mine."

Hogan just licked his lips and waited for another sausage.

Clare Dowling's books include *Fast Forward*, *Expecting Emily*, *Amazing Grace* and *My Fabulous Divorce*.

www.claredowling.co.uk

7. PUPPY LOVE
Clare Dowling

For Ava's thirtieth birthday, Barry presented her with a pet dog. It was an odd-looking animal, with short legs and a stocky little body, and eyes that bulged slightly and fixed upon her malevolently.

"Don't you like him?" Barry asked, pleased as punch. He had tied a pink ribbon around the animal's collar and put him in a basket.

"Of course, he's . . . lovely."

Ava had been rather hoping for an engagement ring. They'd been living together for two years, after all. Still, maybe Christmas. She reached out a hand to pat the dog. His lips peeled back and there was a sudden, wet cracking noise as he bit her.

"My God." Barry was horrified. "Get down, you beast!"

"It's fine."

"Are you sure? Let me see."

"It's okay, honestly." It was just a surface scrape. She had been too fast for him.

Barry wasn't to be reassured. "No, I'll take him straight back to the pound. They told me he was very even-tempered, a model dog."

The dog was now squatting down in his basket meekly.

He looked out at them, shame-faced, as though he wasn't quite sure what had come over him.

"Maybe it was just a one off," Barry ventured, obviously swayed by this display.

Not Ava. She grabbed the dog firmly by the scuff of the neck and opened the back door.

"You can spend the night out there, you lump."

There was a look of surprise on his pudgy, bad-tempered face before she shut the door soundly on him.

"I really hope you two can learn to get on," Barry fretted the following morning, when Ava and the dog studiously ignored each other at breakfast.

"Why?" Ava enquired.

"Well, you're going to be living together now. It's probably just a question of getting used to each other. Look, he's trying to lick your ankles. Isn't he cute?"

So much for taking him back to the pound!

The dog was indeed preoccupied with Ava's ankles. He was crouched under the table, inches from them, poised to strike. She kicked out sharply with one foot. The dog withdrew, but only slightly. Barry grabbed his car keys and stood up.

"Where are you going?"

"Work."

"But it's Saturday." It was also her birthday.

"I know, but there's a report that's urgent."

She looked at the dog. "You're going to leave me with him?"

"It'll give you time to get to know each other." He pressed a kiss on her cheek and was gone. She noted that he smelled of aftershave.

That morning the dog snuck up behind her twice and

tried to bite her ankles. He tore up a cushion and peed on her new Brown Thomas cardigan. Then he caught sight of his own reflection on the television screen and went ballistic, erupting into a volley of strangled barks. When the dog on the screen began to bark back, he started to attack the television like a battering ram.

"Get out, you lump." And out the back door he went again.

Barry came home late. "How did you two get on while I was gone?"

"Don't ask," she said shortly

They went out for a meal for her birthday. When they got back the neighbours complained that the dog had barked the whole street down, at one point drowning out Pat Kenny on the telly. He immediately quietened however when Ava opened the back door and let him in. This time he didn't even try to bite her.

"See?" said Barry. "I think he's taken to you."

He seemed very pleased. Or relieved or something. Then he went off upstairs and she heard him making a muffled phone call.

A week later Barry moved out. He told her, squirming, that he no longer felt the same way about her and that maybe there was somebody else out there for both of them (Fiona from Accounts in his case, as she later found out). He said he hoped she'd be okay. He knew that she was a bit nervous on her own at night, which was why he'd got her the dog. He seemed a little disappointed when she didn't thank him for his consideration.

"What's the dog's name anyway?" her sister Myra enquired when she came around to assess the damage.

"He doesn't have one."

The dog plonked himself down on his fat, moth-eaten bottom, and grinned up at them. One of his teeth was missing from an earlier run-in with the washing machine when it had shifted into spin cycle. Then he began to sniff enthusiastically at his privates.

"He's from the pound." Ava felt compelled to explain.

Myra shook her head. The implication was that at the very least her sister was worth a fluffy Labrador, or a cute Dalmatian.

"What are you going to do with him?"

"I don't know. Send him back, I suppose."

But Lump, as he rapidly became known, seemed to have settled in. Or, rather, he took advantage of her grief and distraction to stealthily take over her home. He began this process by lifting his leg over all the doorframes. Then he constructed a kind of cave for himself in the utility room with various items of her clothing, and those of the neighbours, and would growl ferociously if she came too near. She had to wait until he was asleep before she could sneak in to put on a wash. Then she would retreat upstairs before the machine went into spin, and sent him into a rage.

He ate a lot, too. Pedigree Chum – he turned up his nose at own-brand – and ice cream, and big bags of nuts that cost her a fortune in the local Spar. Then there were the visits to the vet for jabs, and the grooming products and the de-lousing powder after that time she had seen his hair move of its own accord.

Lump was never grateful for any of this of course. He seemed to have forgotten his humble beginnings very quickly and took everything she did for him as expected, and would get into a dreadful snit if she was late home from work or forgot to change the water in his bowl twice a day.

Then he began to object if she went out for the night. He would howl the entire time she was gone, until eventually the neighbours threatened to start up a petition.

"It's getting out of hand," Myra warned. "You're going to have to start training him before he goes to the dogs altogether."

The next morning she took him to the park with a stick.

"Fetch!" She threw the stick.

He looked at her like she was mad.

"Go get the stick, Lump."

He refused point blank. They moved on to basic commands, such as sitting. But he wouldn't sit either.

"Sit, you bugger."

Lump wouldn't. He looked off to the middle distance as though she didn't exist.

"Force him down." A passing jogger had slowed. A big handsome guy in tight sweats and floppy hair. "You have to show him who's boss."

"Oh. Okay." Slightly embarrassed, she put her hand on Lump's scraggly bottom. The guy hung around to watch, jogging on the spot.

"Sit." But now it was a point of honour with Lump to remain standing. He hardened his haunches under her hand and stood firm, even though his knees buckled with the strain.

The guy laughed. "Feisty little fellow."

Ava began to enjoy the exchange. "I've probably just spoiled him."

"Rotten, I'd say." He came forward a step.

Lump began to growl.

Ava apologised. "He can be a bit unfriendly."

"Oh, that's just for show." The guy stooped down to Lump's level. "Hey, buddy! How are you doing?"

There was an ominous rattle from Lump now.

"He can bite," Ava warned.

"With those little bitty teeth? You don't frighten me." He ignored Lump then and said to Ava, smiling widely, "I'm Mark. Pleased to meet you."

"I'm Ava."

He put out his hand to shake hers. It was all too much for Lump. With an unearthly howl, he sprang at the man's throat. The man screamed. Ava screamed too and grabbed Lump's lead. But Lump wrestled the man to the ground as though he were starring in a canine action movie and stood over him triumphantly, while the man lay whimpering under him.

Eventually Ava managed to haul Lump off. She held the lead so tight that his eyes popped. She didn't care.

The man scrambled to his feet, clutching his neck.

Ava said, "Are you okay? Will I get a doctor?"

But the man just staggered away, staring at Lump. "He nearly killed me! He's a fucking monster! "

"I'm so sorry."

"He needs to be put down." And he limped off fast, throwing horrified glances over his shoulder at Lump as he went.

Ava looked furiously at Lump. He panted back at her proudly, obviously under the illusion that he'd saved her from the despicable attentions of a stranger.

Three months later Ava ran into Mark in a pub in town. She hardly recognised him in jeans and a shirt. But he certainly remembered her.

"Vicious piece of work, that dog," he said immediately.

"Yes, I'm really sorry about that." Although in fairness to Lump, Mark had been warned. Twice.

"I hope you had him put down."

"Um, yes." Lump was at that moment over in Myra's, under protest.

Mark nodded grimly. "Good. Because he's dangerous. I wouldn't be happy around an animal like that."

They spent a few minutes at the bar chatting. Then, later, when Ava was leaving, he caught up with her at the door and asked her out to dinner the following weekend. She accepted.

But then there was the problem of Lump.

"I'm not minding him again," Myra declared. "He's after digging up all my begonias."

In the end, she was forced to book him into the local kennels. He went in quite happily until he realised that he was going to be left there.

"Look, it's just this once," Ava pleaded with him. "I swear."

But he howled in outrage as she left, and tried to jump over the six foot fence.

The dinner date went so well that Ava and Mark went to the theatre the following week. And then to a party. Each time, Ava took Lump down to the kennels for the night and tried to convince him that he would have a great time.

Then Mark invited her to spend a weekend on a friend's boat on the Shannon.

"But maybe you think it's too soon," he said, when he noticed her hesitation.

"No, no." She was simply wondering whether the

kennels would keep Lump for a whole weekend. He seemed to be getting used to it; or at least there hadn't been any more incidents since they'd written in his chart that under no circumstances was he to be approached from behind.

She went to the boat on the Shannon. And to Paris for three days, and then to Roscommon for a week for his sister's wedding.

"How come you never ask me to stay over?" Mark enquired one night in her house. Lump was in the kennels.

"Do I not?" she asked, playing for time.

"Anybody would think you were trying to hide something."

"Don't be ridiculous. Stay tonight, if you want," she declared, wondering whether she'd remembered to lock away Lump's dog shampoo in the bathroom.

Naturally, things were bound to come to a head. It happened a couple of weeks later when she hurried into the kennels to pick up Lump after another weekend away with Mark. When they brought him through, they informed her that, regrettably, they could no longer accept him as a client.

"Why? What did he do?" she immediately enquired, giving him a furious look.

"Nothing." Instead they informed her that he was increasingly withdrawn; that he hadn't eaten or drunk anything since she'd left him two days ago. They felt that he was missing her too much and that the enforced separation was, in effect, breaking his spirit.

She snorted. "It's all an act. You know that, don't you? He's only acting like that so that he won't have to come here any more. I can't believe he's taken you in!"

But they were insistent; Ava would have to make other arrangements from now on.

She stormed home with him. The minute they were in the front door, he made straight for his favourite place on the rug in front of the fire with a little yelp of joy.

That did it. Finally she let rip. "You'd have to spoil this for me too, wouldn't you? The first decent man that I've met in ages, and you just can't stand it! Well, you don't own me, you know. I didn't even want you in the first place!"

Lump looked back at her, watchful and quiet. He didn't even roll on his back and pedal his legs in the air like he usually did when he wanted to win her over.

"It wasn't me you missed in the kennels," she told him. "You just missed your comforts."

And she went upstairs and left him on his own. He didn't try to follow her up.

Over the next few days she avoided Mark. Then she sent him a text message saying she had to go away for a few days. On Friday evening, when they were supposed to have been celebrating their six month anniversary, she was stuck on the couch watching Lump attempt to get fresh with the leg of a padded chair.

The doorbell rang. She opened it before she thought to check who was there. It was Mark.

"So you haven't gone away at all?" he said, unsmiling.

"Mark, I'm sorry. I was going to ring you . . ." Behind her, she pulled the door too quickly. Lump hadn't come to investigate yet.

"I get the message, Ava. I'll let you get back to whoever you have in there."

"I don't have anybody in there."

"Oh? What's that panting noise then?"

She listened; Lump had obviously got lucky with the chair leg.

"Look, Mark, there's something I should have told you."

"Oh, spare me, Ava." But he spoke too loudly; there was a fierce growl and then the clatter of claws on the wooden floor as Lump launched himself from the living room and down the hall to the front door.

She did the only thing she could: she stepped out and shut the front door.

There was an almighty thud as seventy pounds of pure rage flung itself against the other side of the door.

"What was that?" Mark enquired.

"Lump."

"Who?"

"My dog. The one who bit you. I told you I got him put down but I just . . . couldn't."

It dawned on her then; she loved him. Lump, that was. But she loved Mark too. How could she possibly choose?

Mark was silent for a moment and then he spoke. "You called him Lump?"

"Well, yes."

"Jesus. Give a dog a bad name!"

"What?"

"You could at least have chosen something noble, like Sam or Rover. Give him something to live up to."

At the other side of the door, Lump was scratching and barking ferociously.

"He's a good guard dog," Mark commented.

She was looking at him now, hands planted on her hips. "I've had to hide him from you for the last six months!"

"And what kind of message is that giving him?" He seemed indignant on Lump's behalf.

"Do you want to try and make friends?" she enquired.

He squared his shoulders and said confidently, "Why not?"

Ava smiled sweetly and handed him the key.

Ciara Elliot is editor of *Confetti* bridal
magazine and fashion editor of
The Sunday Tribune

8. THE BIG CHAT AND THE UNHAPPY CAT

Ciara Elliot

The table was set for a spaghetti dinner. Upon the red and white checked tablecloth were two clean white plates, a decanter of velvety red wine and a vase of fresh garden flowers picked that day. On the floor was a shiny metal cat dish, one half milk, one half cat food. Melanie had been shopping earlier and had come back on the bus, laden down not only with bags of food but also with the makings of the table that she had bought in the small home-wares store in the village – the glasses and the cutlery that she had brought home and polished until they sparkled.

The meal was to be the scene of the first proper chat they would share together in their new home (or at least their new home together, as Michael had already been living here). All mushroom-coloured walls, square plates and matching bedside lamps, the flat had an unlived in, temporary feel, more like the kind of apartment you would see in a catalogue for a mid-price home store than somewhere real people lived.

Feeling like a newly married woman, even though she was only just nineteen, Melanie was already adding her own touches. She had cleaned the windows, mopped the floor, put on fresh bed linen and now that the table was set, she was just about ready to sit down and savour the last of this early summer's day. Darts of dancing golden light were creating painterly impressions on the wall in the background and on the cat's ginger coat as she lay balled up on the L-shaped sofa. Melanie fell into a dreamy pensive mood.

As she gazed distractedly out of the heavy Victorian sash kitchen bay windows, onto the deserted park that lay behind, she wondered what the future held. The Bolognese sauce bubbled lazily in the background and Mishka, her ever-unforgiving Siamese cat, who she'd had since she was ten years old, was now rounding the doorway and making his way to rub against her legs.

Mishka eye-balled her and Melanie sighed. No matter how much she tried to make light of the situation, she was after all, an out of work pregnant art student, barely a year out of school and a recent runaway from home.

What was this new abode? Mishka seemed to be questioning. What's with all these uncarpeted stairs, light switchers-on-timers, institution colours and dividing walls as thin as tissue paper? Can you please take me home now to my nice comfortable house by the sea? I miss my friends.

Pulling her long sandy-blonde hair out of the high pony-tail she had been wearing all day, Melanie sat on the sofa bed, reached for a comb and scowled right back at him. Brushing her hair, she pondered on the last conversation she'd had with her parents before she had packed her bags and left.

"Oh Precious," her father had said, "It's okay, now don't cry. Of course we aren't angry with you, but what will you do about university? We'll deal with it the best we can. You have an auntie in Kings Cross who will know what to do."

Melanie was an only child, the product of two largely unhappy people in a largely unhappy marriage who had done that age-old thing of transferring all of their discontent, along with their massively disproportionate hopes and dreams, onto the one thing they kept most sacred to them – their daughter.

While Melanie had grown up for want of nothing, there had always been pressure on her to be everything to them. When she had met and fallen for Michael, it seemed like all the needs she had been wanting for in her life – the friend, the older brother, the confidante, were embodied in the one person. Of course her parents hadn't liked him from the moment they met him. The cat had also seemed threatened the first time the new boyfriend had pulled up in his shiny swanky motor to bring her out.

She had telephoned Michael from her mobile in her bedroom and spoken to him in hushed tones. "I have to get out of here. Right now. Tonight in fact."

He had picked her up within the hour. She was waiting at the end of the driveway to her house, camouflaged in the shadow of the giant cherry blossom, sitting on an old leather doctor's bag that she had swiped from her father's surgery. Clutching her cat tightly, she looked like a little lost modern-day Holly Golightly.

There's something about girls and cats that I don't quite get, thought Michael as she clambered into the passenger seat, all gangly teenage limbs, freckled nose and long hair. He had hoped that Mishka wasn't going to be a part of this happy package. In the meantime Mishka was already throwing him knowing daggers. Kissing his girl, he patted the cat and was met with a hiss and a spit.

"Oh, Mish, stop that!" said Melanie, gently but firmly. She

pulled down the mirror from its expensive coffee-coloured leather visor and fixed her lips Scarlet Johansson-style.

The three of them (man, girl, and cat) had driven around in silence for a while. Melanie was trying to find words to explain to Michael her exact predicament. He himself was wondering what was ahead of him now in his life. He had a strong sense that he was embarking on a whole new journey, wherever that was going to take him.

While intoxicated with Melanie's old-before-her time wisdom and the fact she was just so pretty in a kind of all-American healthy teenage way, it niggled at him that they didn't know each other very well or for very long, and that there were lots of people out there who would not be happy at all with this new person in his life, least of all his ex wife.

He had secrets he was keeping, such as the fact that he was not actually divorced yet from his wife and nor were they necessarily getting a divorce. In fact they were still at the stage of 'legal separation', and attending couple counselling in an attempt to salvage their marriage which he had walked out on two years previously. She had thrown him out after discovering his extra marital flings.

At the start he had begged his wife to take him back, and although she was having none of it at first, he was slowly winning her affections back. More than a few times they had spent the night together at her place. But somewhere along the way he had met Melanie. This however was an occasion he had chosen not to share with his ex.

So as they drove and stole the odd smile and guilty look from each other, both naughty and secretive in their own sneaky ways, their worlds collided but their future was anything but clear.

Time passed and the silent hours turned into days and then

into weeks until nearly two months had passed, and they were still politely tip-toeing around each other, like actors who share the same dressing room but not the same stage.

Still neither of them had said a word of any meaning, although Michael had been out twice to meet the ex and Melanie had been back to the doctor to receive the unwanted news of pregnancy confirmation. In the meantime they had settled into something of a domestic bliss framed by the joys of cooking and cat keeping.

Tension had been building and tonight they would finally talk. Melanie had sign-posted 'the big chat' as he was on his way out that morning. Michael's recent mysterious experiences had sent shivers down his spine. Her midnight vomiting had not gone unnoticed either and now Michael expected the worst. If warning signs from the movies were to be believed, it meant she was now pregnant but he didn't know if he could choose between her and his ex wife.

Even Mishka could even tell something was afoot. Tonight she was crankier and more attention-seeking than ever, thought Melanie, as she pranced around the flat in figures of eight shapes, rubbing up against everything that stood in her path.

Melanie wasn't quite sure about the desired outcome of the chats either. She knew she wanted Michael to support her decision, be it to keep the baby or to go for that ugly visit to her aunt in London, but she wondered what his reaction would be, and suddenly it crossed her mind that he may have been in a similar situation before.

She wondered what he'd been like in his previous relationship, his marriage to Charlotte the chiropodist, who still texted and left messages on his phone. Melanie reckoned she maybe wasn't quite over him. Michael had made it very clear that their relationship was a disaster. He said they'd fought every day of his marriage. Apparently she hadn't trusted him and finally he'd had enough.

She remembered her first encounter with him. She'd been on a park bench, sketching trees and passers-by, when their paths first crossed. Mishka had followed her out to the park and had climbed to the furthest branches. She'd heard somebody speaking loudly.

'Oh no, not this again. We are going around in circles here. I just don't know.'

The dismembered voice was coming from a shaggy-haired man walking in her direction. He wore a proper suit, had cobalt-blue eyes, and carried an expensive briefcase. He looked a vision of youth and success.

Just at that moment Mishka, who was still up the tree, beginning to whine as she tried to paw her way down, branch by branch, lost her grip, falling to the ground between them with a large thud.

Michael, very used to charming young girls, found this the opportune moment to end the phone call to his ex wife and enter Melanie's life.

Melanie was suddenly woken up from her reverie with a slam to the front door. Michael was back. She heard him coming up the stairs. He entered the room. He looked more handsome than she had ever remembered.

'I've made a decision. I want you to come away with me,' he said. 'How about Mexico? There's a flight leaving tonight.'

'For a holiday?'

'Maybe a holiday. Maybe forever. You know me, I'm not that predictable.'

She knew that alright. Michael was the most unpredictable

person she had ever met. And probably unfaithful too. She wasn't stupid. She knew that he had cheated on his ex wife and would one day do the same to her. Maybe he had already started. What about all those secret phone calls and unexplained disappearances?

Her delayed response seemed to unnerve him. He fidgeted with his keys.

'Well?' he said.

'What about Mishka?'

'What about her? We can't bring her.'

'But I can't leave her here all by herself. She'd starve to death.'

'She can catch mice or something . . .' he gave a nervous laugh. 'Hang on a minute, you can't be serious. Are you telling me that it's a choice between me and a cat?

Melanie took a deep breath. 'That's exactly what I'm telling you Michael,' she said dully. Everything was finally beginning to make sense.

He stood looking at her foolishly.

'Go on, you go and get your flight now. I've made my decision. I'm staying with Mishka.'

Cathy Kelly's books include *Woman to Woman, What She Wants, Someone Like You, She's the One, Always and Forever, Lessons in Heartbreak, Best of Friends* and *Past Secrets*.

www.cathykelly.com

9. TAMSIN
Cathy Kelly

She came into my life bearing distemper, sarcoptic mites and more love than I'd ever imagined. A small bundle of blonde Labrador fur, she chose me that evening. She was the smallest of the litter with the fattest belly and the most beguiling look in her eyes.

I put her into a blanket-lined cardboard box for the journey home but Tamsin decided that she wanted pure non-cardboard love and wanted to sit on my lap, which was pretty much where she sat for the rest of her life. But her proper place will always be in my heart.

My family were always doggy people and had always owned dogs, primarily Red Setters, the canine breed most in need of psychiatry. As a child, I read stories to our beloved dogs, sat in their baskets and treated them like the family members they were. So when I moved out of home, it was natural to me to get a dog. In fact, I got two. When Tamsin came into my life, I already shared house with Demelza, a stunningly beautiful and nervy Red Setter who would have been a pre-Raphaelite beauty if she'd been a human, and who was stone deaf when off the lead. Demelza knew all the naughty tricks, like how to eat a sofa from underneath so nobody noticed.

Tamsin, hugely clever, but the one who was always caught in the middle of mischief-making, was a quick learner. Together, they scratched the putty from the glass kitchen doors and rattled the hell out of teddy bears with manic glee. They sneaked the toothpaste out of the bathroom and ate it, and letters were chewed to pieces as soon as they plopped on the mat.

Once Tamsin's dreaded distemper was gone, the itch started. I went to the vet wondering why the flea unguents weren't working.

The vet, his mouth twitching with humour, wanted to know if the humans were itching as well as the dogs? Indeed, I was black and blue all over from scratching too . . .

Clang, the penny dropped.

Sarcoptic mites, found in infested straw where Tamsin came from, burrow into dog's skin and although they can't live on humans (or so the vet said) they can irritate your skin. Cue smelly washing stuff and no more mites.

It was an inauspicious start to one of the great loves of my life.

Tamsin was always small after her sickly start in life but I don't know if there was ever a dog more loved. And she loved me in return. She was my shadow, coming with me everywhere, sitting in the back of my car wherever I went. Even now, when I drive on my own without my gorgeous little sons, I forget that Tamsin isn't there and talk to her before realising, with great pain, that she's gone.

For thirteen years we were together, through every joy and sorrow in my life. We walked in all weathers, danced through puddles and surged through long grass. She deserved care and respect and she got it.

She could say more with one glance than most people

can with a dictionary. She sat at my feet when I wrote, and when she was too old and stiff to climb the stairs to my office, I helped her upstairs or tried to work downstairs.

She gave me so much love, joy and she taught me how to be a mum. There's nothing like the responsibility of taking care of a beautiful animal with trusting eyes, to teach you how to take care of children.

I would have given everything I owned to keep her with me, but when she was nearly thirteen, and when I was heavily pregnant with my twin sons, she left me. She knew I was pregnant, sniffing my belly, knowing it was going to be different and that it was her time to go. I can't write this without crying, and it would be awful, after all we shared, if I didn't cry for my darling Tamsin.

I haven't had another companion animal since. It's one of the cruellest facts that dogs live such short lives and I don't know if I could bear to lose a creature even half as dear to me as Tamsin. She knew me at my best and my worst, and still loved me.

Two years since her death, my hands automatically reach down to pet every dog I see, and I still find myself gauging people by how they feel about animals. The person embarrassed as they try to lure the cat off the worktop makes me remember my dad's dog, Tara. She was an imperial majesty whose party trick when annoyed, was to clamber onto the kitchen table and lean forward to peer through the glass doors into the dining room hoping to elicit some response. And who could forget Prinny, the rescue dog who was a bundle of platinum Wicklow Collie fluff and was the toughest blonde ever? Woe betide anyone who'd hurt her family.

My love affair with dogs still isn't over and one day, when my heart hurts less over Tamsin, I'd love another small furry body to clamber onto my lap and demand love.

But there will never be another Tamsin.

Pixie Pirelli (aka Kate Thompson)
is the author of *Hard to Choos*.

www.pixiepirelli.com

10. LA-LA LAND
Pixie Pirelli

One fine spring morning, La-La woke me by dropping little kisses on my ears. 'Happy birthday, Marilyn!' she sang. 'Look what I have for you! Presents!'

I stretched, and opened one eye. There, at the foot of my wrought iron sleigh bed, was a pile of gift-wrapped stuff.

'But you're not to open them until after your toilette. Now. What shall we wear today?'

La-La moved to the armoire where she keeps my clothes. I slid off my bed and strolled after her in the buff. I like to sleep naked, but some nights she makes me wear my pink bunny outfit.

'We're going shopping today,' she told me, riffling along the row of outfits that hung in the armoire. 'So you'll want to look smart. Let's see. Well, not this obviously.'

She slid the Fairy Princess costume that I'd worn yesterday to Twinkie's fancy dress party to the far end of the rail, and took down two or three dresses.

'Hmm,' she said, holding a leopard print frock up against me. 'This may be a little heavy for this time of the year. We don't want you perspiring – even though that new deodorizing spray does seem to be doing the trick. How about your Pretty in Pink polka dot? Or shall we go for a more sophisticated look today? Your black and white tube? Yes.'

She set it aside, then started rummaging for accessories. 'Your crystal heart barrette will work nicely with that. And your quilted red velvet pillbox hat.'

She hummed a little tune as she opened my jewellery box, but I was getting bored so I headed to the home gym for a quick workout.

I'd heard La-La boasting about my new gym over the telephone. 'It's called "The Townhouse Gym"' she'd told Twinkie's mistress. 'And it has five large levels, three large lounging pedestals, hanging kitty toys, sisal posts and a large playhouse. It's also beautifully carpeted, with a solid timber frame.'

Leaping onto the fourth floor of the 'Town House', I started battering the crap out of the irritating squeaky canary that fluttered there on a length of elastic. Wham! Take that, my feathered friend! Take that! A right hook went smack on its stupid yellow face. I batted it about for a bit, then went down to the play house area and made short work of one of the Festive Catnip Mice that La-La had put in my Christmas stocking.

My Scratch Buddy scratching post was next. How I loved it! My mistress had acquired it because the copy on the catalogue had told her that it *'Keeps Cats Company As They Scratch And Play To Their Heart's Content'*. Company? As if! The real reason I loved it was because it had this loser fake cat's head stuck on the top, and I could scratch the kitty to kingdom come. The loser cat's ears were torn to shreds, its muzzle was zig-zagged with scars, its eyes were dangling from its sockets. I called my 'Scratch Buddy' Poncy Percy.

All this exertion brought on a fiendish thirst, so off I headed in the direction of my water fountain. As I lapped up the cooled, purified water, I heard La-La calling me. 'Time for your toilette, Marilyn!' I tried unsuccessfully to ignore her, but she descended upon me and swept me up into her arms.

The 'toilette' was an indignity I submitted to in a spirit of compromise. She had tried bathing me once, by stuffing me into a contraption called a 'grooming bag' into which she inserted a shower head, but the heavy-duty black nylon of which the bag was constructed was no match for my claws. The minute that water hit my derrière, I was out of there. She had not tried that mean trick again, but instead wiped me all over every day with a product called 'Nature's Miracle Pet Wipes', about which there was nothing natural nor miraculous.

She would then brush me and spray me with 'Four Paws' cologne, before wrapping me in my silky satin lounge robe. This was trimmed with pink fur, and I often wondered what unfortunate animal provided the trimming. Despite the fact that La-La often dressed me up as a pink rabbit, I was reasonably certain that such a creature did not exist.

'Come along! It's time to unwrap your pressies!' she trilled, hefting me across the room and depositing me on my bed. I laid into the gift wrap with gusto, ripping it to shreds with my teeth and my claws. Here is a list of what the parcels contained:

Item: One feather-trimmed lambswool sweater in baby blue with matching ribbed tam o'shanter plus pompom.

Item: One cherry faux mink coat, also with pompoms.

Item: One blue and silver glass bead necklace with a Swarovski crystal charm, and pearl clasp.

Item: One party tutu of white ruffle spandex and multi-layered pink tulle with armholes for easy on and off.

Hello? Hasn't my mistress noticed yet that I don't have arms?

'It was premiered at the 2004 Golden Needle awards in Beverley Hills!' La-La pronounced with pride, stroking the glittering spandex.

The last item to be divested of its paw-print patterned gift wrap was a plastic box with a picture on it of a cat watching television.

'It's a DVD,' La-La told me. 'Listen to this. She turned the thing called a DVD over, and scanned the words on the back.

'"*Your cats will feel like they are enjoying the outdoors from the comfort and protection of their home,*"' she told me happily. '"*With special guests Ben and Betty Bird, Bonnie Butterfly, Charles the Chipmunk, Freddy Fish, Gary Gerbil, Paulie Parrot and Sammy Squirrel.*" *Now! Let's have break- fast, and then I can take you shopping. I've ordered something very special indeed for you in Whiskers, and I have to pick it up today. Will we go in the pink tote bag? Or would you prefer to be chauffeured in your stroller?*'

La-La slung me over her shoulder, and I flopped oblig- ingly, my head bob bob bobbing as she stomped down the stairs to the dining room. A rumour was doing the rounds on the show circuit that they were working on inventing a species of feline even floppier than the Ragdoll breed that had emerged three or four generations ago. Therefore all us cats were taking care to keep our claws in and grin and bear it when we were obliged to segue into fur stole mode.

When La-La set me down, I shimmied over to my feeding station and examined the contents of my porcelain bowl. Hmm. Minced chicken, a few flakes of wild salmon, and a milky choccie treat for afters. Pah! What wouldn't I give for a taste of fresh pigeon's blood, or a nice juicy rat's eyeball? What wouldn't I give to juggle a live mouse between my paws instead of a catnip substitute, or sink my teeth into the jugular of a quivering baby rabbit? What wouldn't I give to raid a black-bird's nest, or stalk an unsuspecting ornamental duck?

La-La slid her palm along my back, and baby-talked a bit. 'Who's a gorgeous girl? Who's a gorgeous girl? Who's going to look even more gorgeous at her birthday party this evening?'

So I was having a birthday party? It was the first I'd heard of it. Hopefully it would be a bit livelier than Cha-Cha's beach bash last week. A load of Ragdolls dressed in muu muus had been at that barbeque, and had provided their humans with hours of amusement by allowing themselves to be used as beach-balls. I suspected La-La would have loved to have tried something similar with me, but since the incident with the shower head and the grooming bag – when I inadvertently showed my true colours – I don't think she had the nerve. I disguised my disdain for the Ragdolls on that occasion by concealing my expression beneath the peak of my Kitty Klub baseball cap.

'Now, snookums. Eat up, and we'll be on our way.' Click-clacking out into the hall, I heard her say, 'the stroller, I think. All the better to show you off.'

A couple of hours later we emerged from Whiskers boutique, my mistress swinging a couple of glossy carrier bags by their silk handles.

'Another treat, Marilyn! We're meeting Charmelle and the lovely Clive for lunch at Chez Jules,' she told me. 'So let's make sure your hat is on at a becoming angle.'

She leaned over the canopy of the stroller and adjusted my red velvet pill box affair, then sniffed. 'Hmm. A little more *Four Paws* wouldn't go amiss,' she said, producing the cologne spritzer and misting me with the feline equivalent of Chanel No 5. 'And perhaps you're a teensy bit too hot? We don't want your hairstyle to go flat. This should do the trick.' She reached out one of her sparkly pink talons and switched on the battery-operated fan that she kept in my stroller during hot weather. 'There! You look fabulous!'

Click clack, click clack, she went down the Boulevard, until we reached Chez Jules. Charmelle and Clive were there already. I could only see Charmelle's curiously hairless, shiny legs from under the canopy of my stroller, but Clive was displayed to full advantage behind his mesh screen. He was wearing a spotty red bow tie; a blazer with a Kitty Klub crest on the breast pocket, and a straw boater, which was set at a jaunty angle on his furry head. He looked as if he'd just been stuffed by LA's top taxidermist.

'Hello, Marilyn,' he said. 'I'm looking forward to your party tonight.'

'Who invited you?' I returned with a curl of my lip.

'Your mistress,' he said, with a smug smile. 'She has plans for you and me.'

'In your dreams, buster,' I told him. But curiosity got the better of me. I know all about the old adage, but being curious hadn't killed me yet. 'What plans?'

'Wouldn't you just luurve to know?' And Clive lowered his head, and started washing the furry bit between the lapels of his blazer, humming a little tune as he did so.

I set about cleaning my paws, pretending I wasn't interested in Clive's stupid news, and as I groomed, I heard my mistress chittering on above me.

'Look at this!' she said. I heard the tantalizing rustle of tissue paper as she rummaged in the Whiskers bag, and my claws automatically slid out from their sheaths. 'It's called the "Samantha" party frock, and I'm going to dress Marilyn up in it tonight. See what it says on the catalogue? '"*Sexy and stylish. This dress will put you at the top of the 'Best Dressed' list!*"'

'Ooh! It is sexy,' said Charmelle. I could see her hands with their glittering rings take hold of the frock. She held it out level with the table top, and the "Samantha" dress was clear in my line of vision. It was of black spotted net, with a red tulle underskirt, very sticky-out and frou-frou, and I knew it would display my ass to its fullest advantage. I whimpered a bit. There was only so much degradation a gal could take in return for a life of luxury, after all.

'I've ordered the wedding dress,' said my mistress in a theatrical whisper. 'And her going away outfit, and I've booked the Kitty Plaza for the honeymoon.'

What?

'Good. So we're up to speed, then.'

'You won't forget to bring the engagement bracelet along tonight, will you?'

Whaaaaat?

I looked across at Clive, whose chest fur was all fluffed up from washing. He was smiling an inscrutable smile, and I now recognized the tune he'd been humming. It was *The Bells are Ringing for Me and my Gal.*

I looked back at the 'Samantha' dress, swinging from between Charmelle's claws. Its spangles were glinting in the sun, and it looked as if it were inhabited by an invisible, provocatively dancing showgirl.

And as I thought Nooooooo, Clive gave me a slow wink.

He looked like a cat ventriloquist's dummy I had once seen on television. I bared my teeth at him, shook off my pill box hat, then unsheathed my claws. Slash! A swipe with my right paw across the steel mesh screen produced no result. I wasn't going to get out of this prison by force.

'What's wrong with Marilyn?' Charmelle's face appeared framed upside-down at the entrance to my stroller. I essayed a piteous howl. 'Marilyn seems upset by something, sweetie.'

'Oh?' La-La slid off her chair and hunkered down in front of me. 'What is it, baby? Are you missing mommy?'

'Mmm,' I squeaked, looking up at her with eyes like my hero, Puss-in-Boots from *Shrek 2*.

'Oh, baby – come to Mommy. Come on, snookums.'

Result!

La-La undid the metal bolt on the door of my stroller, and unfastened the clasps on my restraint. But before she could gather me to her bosom, I made my bid for freedom. Springing from my stroller, I took off down the Boulevard, swift as the fabled cheetah from whom I was descended. And as I legged it, I heard La-La's voice squealing in panic: 'Marilyn! Marilyn! Come back, come back, come baaack . . .'

I shot a look over my shoulder, and what I saw remains to this day imprinted in my memory. Charmelle and La-La were jumping up and down, hollering and waving; the Chez Jules bus-boy was huffing and puffing along the sidewalk in futile pursuit of me, and Clive was sitting bolt upright in his stroller, an expression of stark incredulity on his face.

When I judged that I'd put enough distance between me and the red-faced bus-boy, I peeled off into an alleyway and managed to wriggle out of my too-tight black and white tube dress. Then I continued on my way, stark naked in my golden pelt, towards the wrong side of town.

'Hey, honey!' A louche-looking chancer leered at me from a doorway. 'Need any company?'

'Sugar, sugar! What's a classy-looking dame like you doing in this neighbourhood?'

'Puss, puss, puss! Cat got your tongue?'

'Hey, baby.' A big black cat was sitting on top of a trash can. One eye was half-closed, a ragged ear drooped, a scar ran the length of his broad nose. He regarded me for a long moment, assessing, and then he leapt down from his vantage point. I could see powerful muscles bunch under his dark fur as he landed soundlessly beside me, and as he circled me, I registered his feral scent.

Holding my head proudly, I tried not to look like a scaredy cat, and then I heard the big black dude say, 'back off, boys! Lighten up and mind your manners. Don't you know how to talk to a lady?'

The alley-cats looked a bit mutinous, but they did as he commanded. We were face to face now. He touched the tip of his nose to mine, and then he slid the side of his mouth along my cheekbone and licked my neck. 'Fancy a bite to eat? I know a good diner not far from here.' He nodded towards the far end of the alleyway

'What's it called?' I asked.

'*The Roadkill*,' he told me.

'Sounds good,' I said, with a smile.

We still go there sometimes, on special occasions – like our anniversary. But we don't go as often as we used to, now that there are mouths to be fed. Leroy works hard, scavenging from bins outside restaurants on the east side. And I have the kittens to rear. They're beautiful kittens, bonny and badly behaved – the way kittens should be.

Sometimes, when I'm lying curled up against Leroy, I think of my mistress and feel a bit sorry for her. But then I think of Clive and the kittens we may or may not have conceived on our honeymoon in the Kitty Plaza, and I think of how those kittens would have been dressed up in frilly bonnets and bibs and tuckers and sold into slavery, as I was. Then I snuggle closer into Leroy, thanking the great Cat Goddess, Ra, for my Great Escape from La-La Land.

Amanda Brunker is a television personality and a top columnist with *The Sunday World* Her debut novel is called *Champagne Kisses*.

11. A GIRL'S BEST FRIEND
Amanda Brunker

Although I love her, my pal Susie is a little bitch. Whenever we're out, she's a typical loud-mouth show-off, demanding attention wherever we go.

Whether with family or strangers, I'm always overlooked as Miss Susie takes centre stage. Admittedly, I've got quite used to being her sidekick, but at times it kills me to know that no matter what revealing outfit I wear, people always look at her and comment on how gorgeous she is. And although I regularly give her a hand doing her hair, she always looks more groomed than I do.

When it comes to meeting men, Susie is my idol as she never shows any fear. Just last week we were out enjoying a good gossip with our friend Joan over an ice-cream. Afterwards we wandered down a quiet street and stumbled across an angry-looking group of youths. Naturally myself and Joan were about to turn on our heels and bolt. But Susie, however, started to throw a few shapes, flicked her blonde wavy highlights in that effortlessly seductive way she has, and ran straight over to one of the gang leaders.

As Joan and myself winced from behind our cupped hands, Susie did her excited little skip, sniffed the stranger's private parts before squatting on the street. After she had finished her lengthy pee across the pavement, the bad boy leader of the gang had instantly fallen in love with her.

Although she's seen it all before, Joan is forever mirroring my pitiful jealousy by turning to me and asking, 'Why can't we get men to fall at our feet like that?'

Of course this little male magnet was born with natural charisma, and has always been able to drive the boys wild with distraction on our street. I try and kid myself that she has just learnt it all from her mistress because I, after all, am a sexy, hot, twenty-something, independent female. The only problem is that I'm a little too independent. At least, I prefer to be called 'independent' rather than 'single', 'desperate' or 'lonely'.

Although, they say that dogs often grow to look like their owners (or maybe we start to look like them!), Susie and myself could only be described as polar opposites. We share a passion for creature comforts and Jaffa Cakes, but apart from that we have very little in common. I can deny her all I want, but as soon as I try to hide goodies from the little bitch, her expert nose can sniff them out of any shopping bag. It's no use trying to catch up with her. She's always half way off down the garden, her mouth stuffed, before I'm even finished locking up the car.

For three years now, we've lived a fairly uneventful life together at number 22 Love Lane. Disappointingly however, neither of us has had a lasting relationship to make us worthy of such a post code! Susie has fared slightly better than I have. At least I know for a fact that the burly German Shepherd at the end of the cul-de-sac, has always carried an unrequited torch for her! Apart from him though, it's been a life of relative celibacy for both of us over the past few years.

There was of course my brief dalliance with a guy called Colin but you could hardly classify that as a relationship. I used to call him my vitamin C as I was convinced I'd be sick without him. However, after a while I copped on to myself and realised that his penchant for treating me like crap only fuelled my obsession to try and change him into that perfect boyfriend. After too much time spent getting nowhere, I finally decided he was just one of my bad habits and broke it off.

After that short union I'd spend night after night sitting by the phone waiting for his call. Sometimes in bed I would wake up to the sound of a text message beeping in my face. 'Babe R U awake?' And yes I always did seem to be awake, thanks to him.

Colin was a music producer. And yes I know that sounds very glamorous, but in reality it's not. Okay, he got to hang out and jam with gorgeous Samantha Mumba-types, and the guys from Coldplay were apparently flying him out to work on their new album. However, as far as I was concerned, the thrill of being able to say, 'I'm with the band', eventually wore thin.

If it hadn't been for his smouldering cheeky grin (think George Clooney, girls!), we would never have survived past the first date. Starting as he obviously meant to go on, he arrived exactly half an hour late. And then in his own derogatory way, he'd make me feel self-conscious about my appearance with niggling comments like, 'Don't eat that, you'd look great if you lost even five pounds,' or, 'You look just like my mother. She has the same coat as you.' Gee thanks!

But it was after he'd missed a dinner party thrown in his honour to meet my mates, I realised enough was enough.

His excuse was that he'd had to meet a band over from London. Yeah right!

I had to be honest with myself. After three months my friends had quite rightly started to call him 'Covert Colin' as they had never even glimpsed the Casanova. So after much soul searching and some encouraging growls from Susie, we finally ditched the rotter.

The weeks that followed were testing. And don't even get me started about my eighty-a-week Marlboro Lights addiction and my weakness to phoning Psychics Online. Lent was a momentous detox to overhaul the mind, body and purse!

Of course my poor pup took the initial brunt of my life adjustments, as the Monday blues weren't confined to just a day, but rather spread across the entire week. Instead of experiencing mad nights out downing double vodkas and Red Bulls with my VBFs Joan, Ciaran and Louise in Renards, my loveless, luckless life became decidedly exhausting.

My mother would call saying, 'darling, you're being so brave,' and 'I told you he was no good for you', while my friends kept a text vigil to inspire my will to live with inanely dull messages like, '2nite let's get da spirits down 2 get da spirits up!' and, 'Plenty more fish in da C'. I took to hibernating under a duvet on the couch with an equally frustrated Susie pining at my feet for a walk in the park!

For the first week I cried off sick at work, whingeing to my boss that I wasn't feeling very well.'You know me,' I explained, 'I don't do sick but I'm feeling very weak and I think it could be contagious. I should really stay away from my office for a few days to try and get better.' Thankfully he agreed.

As my depression persisted into a second week, I concocted yet another fib about a sick relative, which bought me more time off. However disaster was about to strike. Susie, the poor mite, cut herself during one of her bewitching-hour moments after slipping on the polished floorboards. She slid into an embarrassing amount of empty Pinot Grigio bottles. Her terrified yelps could obviously be heard throughout the street. Mrs Doyle from two doors down even left her curtain-twitching post to knock and ask whether somebody had been murdered. As if my nosy neighbour wasn't irritating enough, Omar the local pizza delivery boy with very little English, managed to shower me with some genuine sympathy. 'You OK lady?'

Poor Susie turned out to be fine and recovered. But it was when I noticed that she had grown a junk food potbelly and had become as listless as me, that I truly felt like a bad mother. Of course she couldn't tell me to cop on and get over myself but I knew what she was thinking. I decided once and for all to stop wallowing in self-pity, snapped myself back into reality and cried the last of my last tears.

I owed it to Susie to get my life back on. She, after all, was my most valued buddy. She had always enriched my life, loved me regardless and what was I doing to repay her? I couldn't keep neglecting the girl, and hang about the place feeling sorry for myself. Further inspired by a draining phone call from Joan where she went on and on about her kids and Gerry Junior's bed wetting, I looked over at Susie and said, 'okay pal, let's get ourselves some excitement!'

With a rejuvenated passion we took to power walking in the evenings, straight after Coronation Street in the hope of bumping into some fine things, but the only folk we met were older women with excess saddlebags, and strange men on bikes. I decided drastic action was needed. And then we discovered the *Evening Herald* small ads.

At first the sometimes ridiculous ads seemed amusing as we sat outside the café around the corner from where we lived, enjoying the atmosphere over coffee as the cute waiters called me 'Madame'. It was pleasant whiling away the days but the sniff of stale tobacco from the smelly-arty types who sat over their one double espresso, puffing away, reminded me how much I missed smoking.

Instead of falling back on old habits however, feeling somewhat more empowered, myself and Susie discovered new routes to strut our stuff, and took up people-watching along the more fragrant Dublin canals. There I got to watch the handsome well-spoken office types march home while shouting, 'Trevor!' or, 'Phelim, let's hook up for a few during the week, man!' on their mobile phones while carrying sad little Marks & Spencer dinner-for-one bags. Note to self: must start shopping at Marks & Spencer.

Life gradually got a lot better but as the days went on, I still hadn't mustered up the courage to contact anyone from the small ads. I have to get a move on, I told myself. But the thought fairly terrified me. It was along the banks of the Grand Canal at Baggot Street one sunny evening that I finally mustered up the courage to get in contact with one of the prospective men. He sounded okay. Dublin, male, 32, non-smoking, professional, seeks dog lover. Must be kind, sensitive and enjoy the finer things in life. The right candidate will be showered with flowers, love and free tickets to any concert at The Point.

Immediately he sounded heavenly. A dog lover! I smiled to myself. He might even come with a new pal for Susie. Yes, this guy certainly sounded perfect. Shaking, I dialled the number and sounding like a teenage schoolgirl, I left a cringing, stumbling, mumbling message.

'Eh, hi, em, my name is Lisa, and I've never done this before, so I don't want you to think that I'm some psycho bird who normally calls up strange men . . . not that people who answer ads, or place ads for that matter are freaks or anything. Em . . . sorry this is a bad start . . . . Anyways, I'm a big dog lover. My best pal is a sexy mongrel called Susie, and em, as for me? I've a huge personality. Haha! Call me.'

After an agonising wait of about six and a half hours, I finally got a text message from Box Number 20235. His name was Brian AND he wanted to meet up. I couldn't believe my luck, and neither could Susie. We were both happy.

After several witty text exchanges 'Bootylicious Brian' and his four-legged companion, Gucci, asked if I wanted to share 'A bottle of Laurent Perrier Rose @ Fitzers on Dawson Street. And don't 4get 2 bring baby Susie.'

Admittedly in hindsight I should have forecast some sort of surprise, but totally fixed on the idea that a man – any man – was keen enough to meet me, I had my body spray-tanned head to toe and also got my hair impressively quaffed at Toni & Guy with one of the more expensive senior stylists. And not wanting Susie to be left out, in a moment of giddy madness, I even purchased a garish diamante collar for her.

That Saturday, feeling a million dollars in a stunning Karen Millen outfit, myself and Susie (in her 'Pampered Pooch' bling) walked into town for the double date that was about to change our lives.

Despite arriving fashionably late at the 'Smith' table for two, we disappointingly arrived first. That of course was enough to send shivers down my spine. Was Brian going to turn up at all or had he decided to scarper?

After quickly checking my hair and make-up, and removing a bit of sleep from Susie's eyes, we sat and casually ordered a still water. There was no point in ordering anything stronger in case this supposedly Mr Wonderful stood us up. Probably sensing my anxiety, Susie was on her best behaviour and settled herself primly beside my feet. I waited a while longer trying my best not to keep checking my watch. Where was this guy? If he didn't turn up I'd never live it down. Just as my relaxed, confident posture had started to wilt, I felt a firm hand on my shoulder. As I turned around to get a look at its owner I heard a wonderfully camp voice going, 'so are you my fabulous Miss Lisa?'

As I came face-to-face with my date, my cool grimace turned to a broad, slightly panicked smile. Who was this fabulous specimen in front of me?

Standing at least six foot tall, and dressed in low-hung ripped Levis and a pink faded t-shirt complete with Colin Farrell wristbands, he looked like David Beckham, and strangely enough even sounded like him! Somewhat shocked I sat staring at him, frozen into silence. After all, I had been expecting someone straight. What was this all about? Having said that, all the hints had been there – I'd just ignored them! Brian stood comically with one hand on his hip waiting for my reaction. Both Susie and Gucci had started to make friends under the table but I was racking my brains trying to figure out what to say. Terrified of coming across as rude, I finally blurted out, 'Wow, you're fabulous!'

His reaction was to pull up a chair and agree. 'Yes, I am darling!' he smiled.

Several bottles of pink champagne later, I had learned that Gucci, in a former life had been a terribly neglected stray. Brian was a crazy animal lover which is why he hadn't had the heart to ignore my message. 'You sounded like you needed someone to love you. I couldn't have walked away.'

I, of course, had mistakenly searched through the 'Male to Male' instead of 'Male to Female' ads. Brian was not buying that as an excuse however. 'Oh come on petal. Admit you wanted a gay man to shower you with affection. We're sooo much better at it than those pesky heteros!'

I'm glad to say we really hit it off. Amazingly Susie and Gucci hit it off too. Deep down I think it was the sparkly neck collar that did it for Susie. Gucci was such a stylish pedigree! Together all four of us make a dynamic little family. Six months on now and we are still the best of mates, though Brian and myself are without doubt the biggest bitches. Not in public though – we only bitch in the comfort and safety of our own homes.

Unlike the previous men in my life, Brian is dependable. He adores Susie as much as me, which is brilliant. Of course, we're an odd bunch to look at, and Mrs Doyle from number 26 never fails to throw us an evil glare every time we skip down the road singing, 'We are fam-i-ly. Yeah – hey!'

Do I wish Mr Right had walked into my life that sunny afternoon instead of Mr Fabulous? Of course I do. But how can I complain? As Brian says, 'We're too pretty to be sad. And without boys, we'd have nothing to moan about!'

Marian Keyes' books include *Watermelon, Lucy Sullivan is Getting Married, Rachel's Holiday, Last Chance Saloon, Sushi for Beginners, The Other Side of the Story, This Charming Man, Under The Duvet, Further Under The Duvet* and *Anybody out There?*

www.mariankeyes.com

12. PATCH AND SOX
Marian Keyes

I have two lovely dogs called Patch and Sox. They're black and white – a cross between sheepdogs and King Charles spaniels. Patch is mostly black with a white patch over his eye and Sox is mostly black, but with three white feet (he is not a three-footed dog – he has four feet, the fourth foot being black.) They are good-natured, affectionate and quick to forgive. They are also imaginary. This is because a) I am terrified of real dogs and b) my husband (Himself) loves dogs. Having imaginary dogs was the only compromise we could agree on. It's wonderful having imaginary dogs because if it's raining you only have to take them for an imaginary walk. Also you can go away for weeks on end and they can either come with you or stay at home and eat imaginary meals.

Patch and Sox are basically very good little dogs, but the arrival of Javier and Jesus threw our world into disarray. Javier and Jesus are imaginary Peruvian llamas (the long-necked animals, not the holy men) and they came into our lives via a Mercedes SL convertible. For reasons unclear, Himself's dream car was being built in the Andes, and Javier and Jesus were in charge of delivering it. However, they were so taken with the car that, instead of crating it up and putting it on a ship, they decided to drive the car to us in Dublin.

So leaving their wives, girlfriends and children behind they set off on the mother of all road trips. They put the roof down and shagged and caroused their way up the Pan-American Highway and across the United States. And when they got to New York, somehow they managed, not only to stow away on the QE2, but to pass themselves off as two rich Peruvian playboys. Most nights they took their dinner at the Captain's table and caused mayhem by subverting the table display classes – where bizarrely, Paul Burrell was the demonstrator. Paul Burrell would go to the not-inconsiderable trouble of converting a white linen napkin into a perfect rose and immediately Jesus would shake it out with a sharp crack, spit on it and pretend to be Javier's mother cleaning his face before going to school. And that wasn't all they did with the napkins. It got worse. They wiped other body parts with them, not just their faces. Mutterings about their inappropriate behaviour spread through the ship. Complaints were made but at this stage too many people were afraid of them for a stop to be brought to their gallop.

They arrived at our house in Dublin early one February morning. Himself was so thrilled to get his new car that he insisted that Javier and Jesus stay with us as long as they liked, to recover from their 'arduous' trip.

I disliked them on sight. Javier chewed coco leaves constantly, used everything as a spittoon and had a unpleasant, menacing smile which displayed his long yellow teeth. Jesus barely spoke to me and when he did, he addressed all remarks to my cleavage. They expected me to wait on them hand and foot.

They went out every night at about eleven to Lillies and

Renards and arrived back at five in the morning, where they invariably woke the whole house, looking for someone to pay the taxi driver. More often than not, we also had to pay the extra twenty euro 'soiling charge.'

Then they'd lounge all day long on the couch, with their legs wide apart, scratching their nethers and smoking cigars that they'd stolen from the QE2's humidor. Their conversation was coarse and crude and they never seemed to sleep.

I hated them and was desperate for them to leave, but Patch and Sox were mesmerised. They'd huddle in the corner, too shy to come nearer, hanging onto the llamas' every vulgar word. This worried me. They were innocent little creatures who were being introduced to a world of which they'd previously had no knowledge. However when I suggested in a high, over-bright voice that they go and play outside, they got quite huffy with me.

Eventually I could take no more. In the hope of hastening the llamas' leave-taking, I suggested that their wives back in Peru would be missing them. But Javier made an almost unrepeatable comment that after thirteen children, having sex with his wife was like throwing a chipolata up the Grand Canyon and he was in no hurry home. Javier and Jesus laughed raucously at this and to my horror Patch and Sox joined in. I suspect they didn't really understand what was so funny.

This had gone too far. I bullied Himself into telling the boyos their time was up – there was more chance that they'd listen to a man. They'd never listen to me. But the showdown went very badly and when Himself arrived back, he was close to tears.

"They laughed at me," he said. "They said I was pussy-whipped."

Fury surged up into my mouth. Pussy-whipped, indeed! "Well, you're not, okay?" I yelled. "Say it for me. I am not pussy-whipped."

"I am not pussy-whipped," he muttered obediently.

"Good! Just don't you forget it!"

After that, the dynamic worsened. Javier and Jesus were now openly contemptuous of Himself and myself, and Patch and Sox became ever more brazen. They'd moved out of their shy little huddle in the corner and were fraternising quite freely with the llamas. One morning, I found Sox being taught how to smoke one of the QE2 cigars and when I reprimanded him sharply, he briefly appeared frightened. Then he looked at Jesus, taking his cue from him. Jesus laughed derisively at me and, after a tiny hesitation, Sox also laughed mockingly, aping Jesus's barking scorn and head-back gesture. Then Patch joined in. We've lost them, I thought, my heart pierced with terrible grief. We've lost our innocent little dogs.

But the following morning, when Himself and myself woke, something was different. Yes, we'd been roused as usual at 5:00am, having to cough up the taxi fare and the soiling charge, but we'd gone back to sleep. But now the house was silent. Most mornings we were woken to the groans and squeals of *Debbie Does Dallas* on the video player. Now the acrid smell of cigar smoke was in abeyance and there were no glamour models frolicking in the water feature.

We descended the stairs, barely daring to hope. They'd gone. In high dudgeon. Not even a thank-you note. Also gone was a bottle of Absinthe, two packets of bourbon biscuits (the eejits probably thought there was real bourbon in them), a bottle of Jo Malone Nectarine Blossom and honey scent (Jesus had had his eye on it for one of his girlfriends), a Belleek creamer and sugar bowl (which had been a wedding present), the video player, Himself's fake Hugo Boss watch and – worst of all – Patch and Sox. It was the bitterest of blows. Our lovely little dogs were gone! We wanted to go to the police but were talked out of it. What could we say? Can you put an APB out for two imaginary dogs, who are in the company of two imaginary, albeit deeply unpleasant, llamas?

We moped around the house, heavy at heart. Friends and family tried well-meaning words of comfort. "You can get another pair." But we couldn't. Imaginary dogs aren't like video players. You can't just replace one with another. People who don't have imaginary dogs simply don't understand.

Instead of feeling better, our heartsickness actually worsened, and just when we were at our lowest, amazing news came from my sister Caitriona who lived in New York. Patch and Sox were staying with her! I asked her what had happened to Javier and Jesus and she said, dismissively, "That pair of operators! Tried to sweet-talk their way in. I told them to shag off. I know their type."

New York savvy, you see. She had plenty of it. Himself and myself had none. Apparently, after Caitriona refused to let the llamas stay, a big falling out occurred when Patch and Sox wouldn't show their solidarity by leaving with them. An ugly slanging match took place on her doorstep with the llamas telling the dogs that without them they were nothing – just a pair of talentless Mick mutts whom girls wouldn't look at. Patch and Sox argued that before they'd ever met Javier and Jesus, they'd always planned to come to New York and the llamas were lucky to have had their company for so long. Apparently it was like a re-enactment of the Human League's *Don't You Want Me Baby?*

Although Patch and Sox wouldn't come on the phone and talk to us, Caitriona said that they seemed to be in good health and happy to be shot of the llamas. "They're talking about getting into the movies. They've seen some film that's made a big impression on them. Something about Dallas?"

She rang back a few days later. "Porn," she said. "They want to make porn films. They're pretending to be twins. They say that twins are very popular in porn films. They've already got an agent. I think they'll probably do very well at this."

She added that she could imagine our distress but advised us to let them go. "Let them do their elastic band thing," she advised, "and maybe they'll eventually come back to you."

So what could we do? It was probably the hardest thing we'd ever done, but we didn't interfere. We missed the little pair of scamps, but we tried to be glad that they were making their way in the world and were fulfilling their dreams.

We got on with our lives, ever aware of the Patch and Sox-shaped hole, but trying our best to be brave. So imagine our surprise when we went to the cinema to see *The Day After Tomorrow* and there they were, up on the silver screen. They belong to the homeless man in it – he only has one dog but because of the laws limiting the hours animals can work, both of them played the one dog.

They looked wonderful, although obviously a little more glossy than we remembered. Himself insisted that Sox had had collagen injections in his ears, that they were never that plump and swingy before but I said it could be just down to good lighting. Nevertheless, plastic surgery or no plastic surgery, they'd made it big, even it if wasn't in porn, as they'd hoped for. We were able to be happy for them and yes, even a little proud.

Shortly after that, more news arrived from Caitriona in New York: Patch and Sox had done a moonlight flit. They'd skipped off, leaving a massive phone bill and several outstanding movies on her Pay Per View. Obviously we were horrified and offered to pay the outstanding sums, but she wouldn't hear of it. They had more than enough money of their own. She said they could and should pay their own way. However, she admitted that she had no idea where they'd gone. One of their friends (a duck-billed platypus) insisted they'd headed west, to Los Angeles, but another (a know-all meerkat) said they'd definitely gone south, to Dallas. But they could be anywhere, Caitriona said. Anywhere other than Peru.

As it happened, they were headed for – of all places – Dublin! They showed up at our door one Wednesday, around teatime, looking suitably sheepish and bearing peace offerings: a mug (with a chip out of it) saying 'I heart the Big Apple'; a snowdome of Bloomingdales; a bar of Hershey's chocolate with three squares missing and a t-shirt saying, 'My imaginary dogs went to New York and all I got was this lousy phone-bill.'

Himself and myself tried to make them grovel but they were so apologetic and they'd been through so much. Patch had had his head turned by the tawdry glitter of show business and had succumbed to cocaine addiction. All their earnings had been spent on a month's rehab for him in upstate New York. They were very disillusioned with the movie business. A shallow world of instant gratification was how Patch described it. "We're so sorry," they said. "We just want to come home."

As soon as they'd promised to pay Caitriona back her money, all was forgiven. They settled back in immediately, although they have some new habits picked up on their travels. For example, they're very fond of Itsa Bagel in the Pavilion in Dun Laoghaire! We're as happy as we ever were and you'd swear they'd never been away. If ever there's a mention of llamas or Machu Picchu or anything to do with Peru, they blush a little and become manifestly uncomfortable. But Himself and myself say nothing. They've learnt their lesson and there's no need to rub their noses in it.

Tracy Culleton's novels include *Looking Good, Loving Lucy* and *More than Friends*.

www.tracyculleton.com

13. PAWS FOR EFFECT
Tracy Culleton

In memory of Mitzi, my best ever cold-nosed friend, and Cassidy who wasn't far behind.

Mitzi (Cocker spaniel) and I (human) were out for a walk when I observed a tall attractive man putting up a notice outside the parish centre. Intrigued, I went over for a closer look.

"Our family friend Stella is running obedience classes for dogs," he told me. "They're starting next Monday."

"Brilliant! Mitzi here is far from well-trained! I think I'll enrol."

Ignoring Mitzi's shocked and reproachful expression at this news, I glanced at the handsome stranger to see his reaction.

"Great!" he said enthusiastically, with a heart-crunching smile. And then spoiled it by adding, "Stella will be delighted."

He smiled again and turned and walked away. I twisted to surreptitiously look at him. Broad shoulders – check. Narrow waist – check. Long lean legs topped by a perfect bottom – check. Not to mention three checks for his handsome angular face, fabulous blue eyes and thick dark-brown hair. I sighed a little and turned back to the notice to take down Stella's number.

Accordingly Mitzi and I turned up the following Monday. I had explained to her what was going to be happening, and she wasn't one bit impressed. She liked the status quo, in which coming-when-called was an optional extra.

To my delight and surprise that handsome man was there too, with a glossy black Labrador-cross. He gave a big smile of recognition and came straight over.

"Hi," he said, holding out his hand. "Brian Fox. And this is Cassidy."

"Joy Flynn and Mitzi." We shook hands, or sniffed noses, according to the custom of our respective species.

"Right, Ladies and Gentlemen," called Stella briskly. "Please line up over there with your dogs."

We all hurriedly complied. Whatever about the obedience-quotient of our dogs, we humans were certainly hopping to it when the formidable Stella spoke. Brian and I ended up standing side by side, and I'd no complaints about that.

"Okay," Stella boomed, "I'm going to call each dog in turn and see if it'll come to me. That way I can get an idea of what we're dealing with."

Most of the dogs were over-excited at being in this strange location, and being surrounded by so many other strange dogs. At first there was a lot of leaping and yapping, however eventually most of them did go to Stella when she called them. The doggy treats she was wielding probably had something to do with that.

When it came to Cassidy's turn, he behaved perfectly. He ran straight up to Stella and sat in front of her, his tail wagging proudly. Swot, I thought sourly. Isn't there always one? We were next. This is it, I thought, my heart beating nervously. I so wanted Mitzi to do well. I unclipped her lead and Stella authoritatively called her. But Mitzi stayed exactly where she was. In fact, she began leaning against my leg.

"Mitzi!" called Stella again, "come here girl."

In response Mitzi cowered even more against me.

"Right," said Stella briskly, "I can see we're going to have our work cut out here. Next!"

As my neighbour's dog ran enthusiastically towards Stella, I cringed inside. Being childless I've never had to endure the trauma of reading school reports, but right then I could imagine how it felt. My feelings were a mixture of humili-ation at Mitzi's behaviour, annoyance because she was letting me down, shame at myself for caring so much, frustration at the bad report, but love for her regardless, and a steely determination to do better.

Mitzi, it appeared, didn't really care. Herself and Cassidy were getting to know each other better by sniffing each other in places not usually recommended in polite society.

After the class Brian and I happened to leave together.

"Well," he said, "I'll see you next week."

"See you. Not that you need to be here, of course. Cassidy's so well-behaved."

"Ah well," he said awkwardly, "there's always room for improvement."

Over the next few weeks I found I was looking forward to Monday evenings, which was surprising considering Mitzi remained mostly impervious to Stella's training techniques. I was becoming more and more embarrassed and Stella was getting more and more fraught. So what was there to look forward to? Ah, seeing Brian of course. We automatically stood together now, chatting about the past week's events, and comparing notes about the progress of the dogs. Not surprisingly Brian had a lot more to say on that subject than I did. Each week we left together and parted company with a cheerful goodbye and a "See you next week!" If only he'd ask me out, I thought despairingly. I became a little more despaired with each passing week. After all, this was only a six-week class! If he didn't do it soon, he'd miss his chance. I couldn't understand why he didn't ask me out – he always sought out my company and seemed to enjoy being with me. Maybe I'd have to bite the bullet and ask him out. Mind you, I'd only do that as a last resort. At least Mitzi's behaviour was improving. Sort of.

However, at the end of the sixth week, just as I was about to give up hope, it happened! We were saying goodbye as usual when he said, "I'd love to suggest a coffee or drink to celebrate the end of the classes but that would be fairly impossible with this lot in tow!" He grimaced, indicating towards our two canine companions.

"You're right, they'd never allowed into the pub," I agreed with a smile. "They're both underage!" we suddenly said in unison before creasing up with laughter.

"Maybe, however," he then added casually, "you might like to go out without them some time."

"Yeah, sure, why not?" I said equally as casual.

"How about Wednesday?"

"Sounds good," I agreed lightly.

We met on Wednesday evening and it was absolutely magical. I swear I could hear a whole orchestra in the background playing romantic music as we laughed and chatted and smooched our way through our first date. Same thing during our second date on Friday two days later. And our third date on Saturday, the day after that.

On Sunday afternoon we met up for a walk in the Phoenix

Park. The dogs were running ahead of us, enjoying the exotic smells, the space and the freedom.

"So what did you think of the obedience classes?" he asked me. "It seems as if they worked for Mitzi. I've enjoyed watching her progress."

"Well . . ." I prevaricated.

"What?" he asked, intrigued.

"If I tell you, do you promise not to tell Stella?

"Hand on heart."

"Okay. Well, it's true that Mitzi's behaviour has improved during the classes. But I think she's decided that she only has to obey when she's in the parish centre and in Stella's presence. She behaves perfectly there. But once we're outside, she's as bad as ever. She still has her laissez-faire attitude. That hasn't changed. However," I added laughing, "whenever she does deign to come, she does it in style. She doesn't just arrive in my general direction as she used to do. Oh no, she comes right in front of me and sits! Likewise if she does condescend to walk with me, she heels perfectly."

Brian put back his head and laughed uproariously, and even though I laughed too, I did it while simultaneously managing to admire his strong jaw-line and muscular neck.

"But what about your Cassidy?" I asked then. "Honestly, he's really the star of the show. I mean, he was always pretty obedient to begin with, but now he's good enough to win competitions!"

Brian shifted a little, looking extremely uncomfortable. His laughter ceased.

"Joy, can we sit down here a minute?" he asked sombrely, pointing to a bench. "There's something I need to tell you."

"Okay," I said, my heart sinking. I wondered what was wrong. People never speak in that grave tone of voice when they're about to propose marriage. Or when they're planning to offer you a share of their Lotto win. Not that either of those situations has happened to me, I hasten to add.

We sat down, and the dogs, seeing this, flopped at our feet.

"It's like this," he said, "I've a big confession to make."

A thousand possibilities raced through my head in that instant. Had he just realised, after fighting it for years, that he was gay? Was he in fact married? Had he an unsavoury predilection for young girls? Was he wanted by foreign police for fraudulent behaviour, or something more simple, like not paying his TV licence? What was it that he wanted to tell me? Surely he wasn't about to begin a six-month trip to Antartica? Had he accepted a job on an oil rig? Was he off to become a Trappist Monk? Had he a terminal illness?

"What . . . what is it?" I asked tremulously.

He wouldn't meet my eye. He just sat there, his head bowed. Then he took a deep breath. "The truth is, I've been operating under false pretences," he said. "I don't even own a dog. Cassidy belongs to my sister. And you're right – he is already very well trained. Stella, being a family friend, had already whipped him into shape. Not literally, of course," he added quickly.

To be fair, Cassidy, contentedly chewing a stick in front of us, didn't look like a dog that had ever been whipped.

"I don't understand," I said. "Why on earth would you bring Cassidy to the obedience classes? In that case – oh!" I put my hand up to cover my mouth as the realisation hit me.

He turned to look at me then, his expression a mixture of fear, hope and anxiety. "Yes," he said, "I've got to come clean. It was you I wanted to meet. I've liked you from the first moment I met you outside the parish centre. Enrolling in the class seemed like the only way I was going to meet you. So I borrowed Cassidy, and Stella agreed to let us join. She thought Cassidy would be a good example to the others, so she didn't mind. Well," he took a deep breath, "that's it. That's my guilty secret out."

"So you're not gay, or married, or ill, or a fugitive from justice?"

"No. Honestly, no," he said laughing. "So, do you forgive me?"

"Nothing to forgive," I smiled. "It's quite romantic really." With that his face lit up and he bent down and kissed me passionately and thoroughly, and with – if I'm not being over-fanciful – more than a hint of promise about it.

When we came up for air I said, "I'd better confess my own secret, so."

"You have a secret too?" he put his hand to his heart, mock-horrified.

"Yes I do. When I saw you putting up the notice I was curious. However I admit I was more intrigued with you than by any obedience classes. I only enrolled in the hopes of getting enough information about you from Stella. Since you said she was a friend I thought I might be able to bump into you through her."

"Really?"

"Yes, in fact I couldn't believe my luck when you actually turned up at the classes! Now I know why you did though!"

"So you didn't need obedience classes for Mitzi?"

"Well, it wasn't a huge priority. Of course she could probably do with being more disciplined, but we manage to get by. Mitzi, believe it or not, was my excuse to get in contact with you."

I bent to give my dog a rub of gratitude. But she was nowhere to be seen. Cassidy had all-but shredded his stick, and Mitzi had disappeared.

"Oh no! She's wandered off!"

I stood and shouted, "Mitzi! Mitzi! Come here!"

She didn't respond, and after a moment Brian stood too. "Mitzi!" he roared, his strong baritone voice resonating across the field and bushes and trees. It didn't do any good.

About five minutes later, when she was good and ready, Mitzi came trotting up, delighted with herself. She seemed unperturbed to note that we were both red-faced from shouting, and sat elegantly at my feet.

"So was it worth your while joining the obedience classes, then?" asked Brian ironically.

I looked at the totally unabashed dog, sitting there with her tongue flopping out and a grin on her long snout, and then at him – tall and broad and infinitely handsome, kind and humorous and decent. "Oh yes," I smiled. "I think it was well worth it!"

Tara Flynn is an actress/writer/comedian

14. BOXER

Tara Flynn

Nora's heart quickened as she closed in on her prey. Her terry track-suited thighs whisked together as she tore along the beach. They won't get away with it; not on my watch. The pounding in her chest became almost unbearable and a great dose of pure adrenaline surged through her skinny body as she drew alongside the young woman with the lazy black Lab. The woman was bent over, using an old Tesco bag to pick up after her dog. Nora hated it when they were responsible like this. It gave her less ammo; weakened her attack.

Now that she was closer, she realised that the woman wasn't as young as she'd seemed from behind. In fact, she was probably only a decade or so younger than Nora herself. A quick scan of the kinds of voices she would usually have employed (or rather deployed – for Nora, this was a military operation) told her that the schoolmarmish scolding she had mentally prepared would not wash with this 30-something upstart. Her face was bare of makeup and she had sad eyes but, be that as it may, she couldn't possibly have known the sorrow Nora had known. As Nora allowed herself even briefly to consider that sorrow, the familiar hollow in her heart crept open. It was just a twinge now

where once was agony, but that twinge gave Nora her supe-
riority. She could afford a swagger, even in terry track-pants;
her survivor status made her the queen of all she surveyed.
It made her steely in the face of adversity. All other pain
paled in comparison and this endowed her with the power
she only felt at these moments.

"Excuse me!" she said, in a voice even she recognized as
pinched, "there are no dogs allowed on this beach." She
had tried to use the "matter of fact" voice from her mental
store, but the self-satisfied sneer that squawked from her
now made her almost ashamed. Almost.

The younger woman's eyes flashed. "Excuse me?" she
snapped.

Oh no. One of those. She was going to give Nora a fight.
Nora sometimes forgot that dog-owners were prone to a
level of passion Usually seen only in Sicily. They may not
have carried actual stilettos around in their oversized
anoraks, but daggers somehow still managed to shoot from
their eyes. This kind of dog-owner was the sort who would
cite hundreds of thousands of years of nomadic loyalty, and
quote all manner of canine myths; stories reaching all the
way from Greyfriar's Bobby to the anonymous pooches you
read about in evening papers, who wither and die along
with deceased owners on the floors of council flats, rather
than save themselves by consuming those owners' lifeless
bodies.

Yes, yes, thought Nora, we know all that. Best Friend,
blah blah.

The hollow pain shot through her again, so she focused
on the job at hand. She was warming to the fight; the dog-
woman couldn't have been much more than 5'3", and she
was scruffy.

Nora wore her tracksuit only for these missions, but this poor woman obviously didn't belong to any community groups and it didn't matter what she wore. This extra-sartorial status egged Nora on. She could take her on. It might even be enjoyable. Nora drew herself up to as full a height as uneven sand would allow and repeated, "There are no dogs allowed on this beach."

Concise. To the point. That was all she needed to say. She was a missionary on the side of right and the warm glow of smugness began to fill her hollow heart. Better than sherry.

Anger coloured the dog-woman's pale face as she spat back "Says who?"

"Oh, did you not see the signs?" said Nora in her most sanctimonious voice, "a woman was fined €200 on-the-spot last week."

Nora loved the incongruousness of the phrase on-the-spot for misdemeanours pertaining to dogs. After all, it was never Spot's fault.

"I didn't, and I'm here every day," sighed the dog-woman, the lazy black Lab patiently settling at her feet. "What's more, I just took off her lead by a squad car, and the guards never said a word."

Nora started. She felt her own face blanche a little as this flaw appeared in her plan. Surely the guards knew about this new beach law and were behind its enforcement? Where was her back-up? She was only trying to help them.

"Are you sure they saw you?" she stuttered.

"Yes," said the woman. Now it was she who could afford to be concise, but she didn't take that option: "And if they think they can get €200 out of me without warning signs, that's extortion. You can be full sure I'll make a huge stink."

Glancing at the woman's unwashed hair, Nora was quite sure that a stink was exactly what she would make. Nora tried another tack: "I'm only trying to help."

That'd show her.

"There's no need to be angry with me!" she continued. "I'm trying to save you €200. Besides," (this was the big guns) "it's for the children."

Nora felt cheap; she didn't care about the children, and if their parents were going to insist on letting them swim in the most radioactive sea in the world, then a little dog-poo was hardly going to make much difference.

The little woman in the oversized anorak threw back her head and laughed. Really laughed. She was borderline hysterical. Nora realised that she must have heard this catch-all phrase many times before.

"My dog's eight years old!" she hooted, "and she's hardly an attack-mutt. You can't just toss that old crap at everyone!" she gesticulated, waving the Tesco bag (now filled with poo) emphatically as she spoke.

Nora was insulted. The laughter implied that she was stupid. She was anything but.

"Well, speaking of . . . crap," Nora whispered the word, "we can't have dog dirt all over a public area." She said this in her crossest voice, so that her lips tightened up and she had to deliver the word "area" through her nose.

"Ah listen," said the woman, catching her breath from laughing, "if you've spent eight years with your plastic-sheathed hand wrapped around fresh, steaming poo then you want some effing credit for it."

Nora knew she meant something much stronger than effing. "If you really want to play cops 'n' robbers on the beach, then reprimand those idiots who don't pick up, or whose dogs need muzzling. I won't have my day ruined any further by someone who needs to go off and get themselves a life. Have a nice day."

The woman turned and strode off, the poo bag bouncing defiantly against her leg as she walked, the lazy Lab reluctantly trying to keep pace. Nora knew she didn't mean that bit about her having a nice day. She was angry. She most certainly did have a life. But how could she have got her information wrong?

Her certainty had been her strength. Could she have imagined the whole on-the-spot thing? It was true that sometimes her loss overwhelmed her and she got confused. She raced up to the far end of the beach, to where she'd been told this new sign was. Tide notices and pollution readings were all she found. She cursed herself for not checking this out beforehand.

She trudged back to the car-park; no signs. And there, sure enough, was the squad car, still on duty. A couple passed with a black Cocker Spaniel, quickly followed by an old man with a large mutt on a lead. The guards just sat there. Nora felt the smugness seep from her heart, until only the hollow remained once again. It hurt. She repeated the words aloud to herself, "I'm only trying to help."

But it wasn't true. She wanted rid of them. She didn't want to be reminded. This was her beach, too.

Nora had met Henry ten years ago, and she'd only known him for one, but they'd spent all of that short time together. Even her husband said she loved Henry more than him, and maybe she had. She had spotted him through a gate, on one of her walks, an eight-week old boxer puppy with a big, flat head and the cutest splodge of white on the corner of his mouth. It always made him look like he was smiling.

When she asked, the owner said the pup had just been sold, and Nora's eyes had filled with tears. He said he'd let her know if the situation changed. The next day, she'd returned with the intention of paying more for the puppy, but he was nowhere to be seen. She'd cried all the way home, so much so that she almost couldn't make out the two figures waiting on her front steps. The other party had seemingly lost interest and so the little black dog with the big flat head came to live in her house.

She called him Henry. Henry had huge, speckled paws that trampled everything in her beloved garden but she didn't care. They were meant to be together. She knew she spoiled him, but he was her best friend, her whole day. She cut his toast up into exactly eight pieces after she'd buttered it. He liked that. She carved up half-done roasts when he pawed at the oven door for a slice.

Her kids were cross, said she'd even let the dog drive if he asked for the car keys.

He was a beauty; all muscle and full of beans. It took a two-man team to walk him every day. He was loving and lovable, and for all his size he wouldn't hurt a fly. Until, at three months, Henry turned. He turned on dogs he had known all his life. At first Nora ignored it; they must have provoked him. But then he turned on little Fred, the terrier who lived next door. She watched in horror as her lovely boy tore into his old friend, snarling and searching for his jugular, and would not be called off. For just a second, she was sure he'd shot her an evil look. Without thinking, she dived in, extracted Fred and tried to restrain Henry by the collar as Fred fled, never to return.

Nora didn't cry. She was practical and, after all, a model

citizen. She wouldn't have it said she was irresponsible. So, she called the vet. Her kids came with her, because she didn't trust herself to be able to drive home without him.

Henry bounded into the car as usual and sat in the back seat. The young vet diagnosed "canine epilepsy" and Nora nodded her consent to what must inevitably be done.

Even the vet visibly struggled. "What a beautiful animal," he said.

Nora wanted to wail Henry's name aloud but she didn't. For his sake. Her kids held her, but she felt nothing. She dried her eyes, cradled the big flat head on her lap, and soothed and smoothed it until he went asleep for good. She asked if she could bury him at home, and the vet agreed.

Nine years had passed, but Nora still talked to Henry every day. The hole they'd dug for him in the garden was nothing to the hole he'd left in her heart. The pain had changed Nora forever. So while she didn't hate them, these new dogs on the beach, she didn't exactly like to see them either.

Maybe she'd dreamt the on-the-spot fine scenario; maybe those signs she thought she'd read about in the paper had never actually gone up. Maybe she'd just wished they were there. She was a good person. She had a life. Surely she deserved to live it in peace? She was only trying to help, after all. Was it so wrong if the person she was trying to help was herself?

Jacinta McDevitt's books include
*Sign's On, Handle with Care, Excess
Baggage* and *Write a Book in a Year.*

www.jacintamcdevitt.com

15. LOVE ME TENDER
Jacinta McDevitt

James lifted the egg from the boiling water and dropped it into a blue and white striped eggcup. He spread butter thickly on two slices of toast and divided them into soldiers. With a practiced flick he beheaded the egg. Bright, sticky, yellow oozed down the side of the shell and some had splashed onto his cream shirt. James didn't notice. Had he noticed he would have taken up his knife and with the skill of a surgeon removed all traces. Just as he was about to dip a soldier, the doorbell rang.

James rarely had callers. He wiped his rough, chapped hands on a tea towel and shoved them into the pockets of his knit cardigan as he shuffled along the hallway in his slippers. He was still wearing his cap. He rarely took it off. Small wisps of white hair escaped around the edges, like cobwebs. His face had a lived in look. Weathered and leathery. He opened the door slightly to see who was there.

It was a young boy. He was animated. Big chubby cheeks and bright blue eyes.

"Hallo Mister, my name is Alan an' me an' my little sister an' mam have just moved in next door an' we have a pet rabbit called Elvis an' he just escaped an' my mam said not t' bother you but I think Elvis might be hiding in your back field. Can I please have a look for him?"

He finally drew breath.

He was dressed in blue shorts and was bare-chested. Chest and back the colour of acorns. It was a hot, balmy, mid-summer day. But even in the heat the boy was wearing black wellington boots. James guessed they only came off when the lad went to bed. He was amused and intrigued by the young boy.

"Of course you can look for your rabbit. Come on in, lad."

James gestured to the boy to go through the hall and into the kitchen.

"Alan? Is that what you said your name was?"

"Yes. My rabbit is called Elvis and he's gone missing. I have to find him. He's not used to the countryside."

"Right Alan. Don't you worry. We'll find him. What kind of rabbit is Elvis?"

"A white one, white with black trims. About this big." Alan held his two chubby little hands out about three feet apart.

James held in the laughter and thought it would be easy to spot this giant rabbit. Alan looked around the kitchen taking everything in. Eyes darting around the room hopping from the row of Toby jugs on the dresser, to the fox skin rug in front of the range and the heavy cast iron boot scraper propped up against the back door, holding it open. He was hoping to see Elvis.

James tried to go quickly as he stepped out of his slippers and into his muddy gardening shoes that were resting on a sheet of newspaper by the back door.

"Have you no wellies, then?" Alan asked. "I thought all farmers wore wellingtons?"

"Aye, they do. You're right there lad, but I left mine off in the shed and we're in too much of a hurry to catch your rabbit for me to go and get them. These shoes will have to do."

James could hardly keep a straight face. His half-acre garden was hardly a farm.

They searched through the flowerbeds and shrubs but there was no sign of the rabbit. The boy kept calling: "Elvis, come on Elvis. It's me . . . Alan. Come on."

Elvis was turning a deaf ear, wherever he was.

"I know he's here somewhere, Mister." The little boy's lip started to quiver and eyes moistened. James knew that any minute now there'd be tears. He put his hand on the young boy's head and ruffled the blonde silky hair.

"Tell you what!" he said, "Let's you and I stay very, very quiet. If that rabbit thinks it's safe he'll come out and I bet he'll head straight for my new vegetable plot over there." James pointed to a row of bright green, inviting lettuce shoots.

They waited, watching. Sure enough, in no time at all, a little pink wriggling nose appeared from behind the apple tree. James pointed and held his fingers to his lips. The boy stayed quiet. The rabbit felt secure and hopped out, stopped, wriggled his nose then hopped again. Straight for the lettuce. James stared at the rabbit. He couldn't take his eyes off Elvis. He had never seen a rabbit like it. It was huge. A huge white rabbit with a long tuft of pitch black fur right on the top of his head. The black fur was so long that it fell over to one side. His four paws were also covered in masses of black fur. He was definitely wearing his blue suede shoes. No doubt about it, the rabbit was aptly named.

The little boy ran up to it and picked it up by the scruff

of the neck. If the rabbit had opened his mouth there and then and launched into a rendition of "Love me Tender", James wouldn't have been in the least bit surprised.

"You were right Mister, he must like your lettuce. That's prob'ly why he came in here. We don't have lettuce in our garden. In fact, we have nothing only weeds. Mam says it's a pure God forsaken wilderness, whatever that is! Anyway the wilderness is on her list. She has this list you see, list of jobs we have to tackle. It's a mighty long list an' the garden is a long, long way down. We have to do all the mending and fixing in the house first. Whitewashing and painting. Mam says that the windows are ready to fall out and all for the want of a lick of paint. Imagine that Mister. Imagine all the windows falling out? She says we'll never be done fixing. But my mam's great at fixing things."

"Oh, I'm sure you're a great help. With your wellingtons and everything. I'd say you give your daddy a grand help to do all the jobs around the place. Sure you'll have them done in no time".

"Oh no. My dad doesn't do the jobs. Mam does all that. Daddy doesn't live with us anymore. He lives with some lady. He comes to visit us on Saturdays. Well, on the Saturdays that he can. When he's not too busy. Dad's very, very busy you know. He works in an office. I'm going to be a farmer when I grow up."

James was taken aback by the honesty and innocence of the child. He could also see the deep hurt the young boy felt but was too young to understand.

"Alan! Alan!" James could hear the lad's mother calling.

"Come on, Alan, your mother is looking for you," James said. "You'd better get off home. I'm glad we found Elvis. Would you like to take a few fresh eggs in for your mother?"

"Yeah. She's always using eggs to make cakes for me and my sister, Lucy. She makes great cakes."

James waved Alan off. For the rest of the evening he smiled to himself every time he thought of young Alan and Elvis. He hoped the young boy would call again soon. If truth be told, James missed people. Missed the sound of laughter and shouting around the place. He had never married but he regarded his nieces and nephews as his own children. They used to call to visit him all the time when they were younger. Now they were grown up and spread to the four corners of the world. They wrote often and sent photographs and postcards from exotic places. They'd never believe him when he told them Elvis had moved in next door!

Early next morning James went out to collect the eggs.

"Hi Mister!" He heard the friendly voice and was delighted to see Alan's little face peeping in between the hedge.

"Hi Alan, how's Elvis?"

"He's okay. My mam said that the next time he escapes he's finished – 'rabbit stew', she said. So, I have him on a lead. I'm keeping close tabs on him."

"If you have your wellingtons on, you and Elvis could come over and give me a hand to collect these eggs."

"Of course I have my wellies on."

Alan squeezed his small body between the gap in the hedge. It was more of a struggle to squeeze Elvis through.

"We could put a gate in here," Alan called, finally pulling the rabbit through and landing on his bottom with the effort of it all.

"You know, a gate for when me and Elvis come over to see you. It would be much better than me having to shove him in through the hedge all the time."

"Well that's a great idea, Alan, let's put it on the list."

They collected the eggs, put down fresh straw, checked the vegetable patch and picked a huge bunch of sweet smelling flox for Alan's mother.

"My mam will love these," Alan said, staggering behind the huge bouquet. His mother came out to meet them at the gate.

"Alan, they're brilliant." She leant forward and gave her son a kiss as she took the flowers. She ruffled Elvis's fur.

"Hi. I'm Hope. You must be James from next door. I've heard all about you. Thanks for these, the smell reminds me of happy times." She smiled as readily as her son.

She was a tiny person. Small, gentle-featured. Her skin was tanned. Hands red and wrinkled from washing. She wiped them on her jeans and shook James's hand. Then offered him tea and freshly baked Madeira cake. The air was thick with it. James couldn't refuse. Especially when he saw the little girl, Lucy. She was sitting on a big, bright patterned, rug on the kitchen floor. Looking as though any second now she would take off, carpet and all, on some exciting adventure. Her baby blue eyes flashed mischief. She was wearing a pretty blue summer dress but it was covered in sticky crumbs. Everywhere was covered, even her bare toes. She smiled a two-toothed grin up at James, her little face lighting up with the delight of a stranger in the camp.

She grinned at him again and rubbed the chunk of cake she was eating all over her head. Into her tight blond curls, making a halo around her head. She chuckled and James chuckled with her.

"Oh, Lucy, what will I do with you?" Hope said. But she was smiling as she wiped Lucy's fat little hands and face.

Alan giggled. James loved it all. Lucy chuckled again. Planning her next trick, James thought.

"You have the place lovely. It's very colourful." James pointed to the jugs of wild flowers and the vibrant fire engine red, yellow and cobalt blue cushions scattered on the armchairs and couch.

"Oh, it's just cosmetic. I have a lot to do on the place but I'm getting there." Once again the easy smile caught James by surprise.

"Listen, I love pottering around fixing things and I have lots of spare bits of timber and stuff in my shed and too much spare time so I was thinking . . . ."

He was sipping his tea, being careful not to appear to be interfering.

". . . I'd be happy to give you a hand to repair some of the windows and things. It'll give me something to do and if Alan was my helper I'd really enjoy it."

"Please, Mammy, please. Can I be James's helper?"

Lucy clapped her hands and chuckled. She was all on to be a helper too.

"Well, if you're sure you don't mind . . . and you'd have to let me know the minute you got fed up with us . . ."

"I promise I'll let you know." James winked at Alan, then at Lucy.

And so the pattern began. Alan called into James every morning and helped him to collect the eggs. Then they carried the wood, tools and whatever else they needed back to Alan's house. The hammering, gluing and fixing began. Alan handing up the nails, marking the wood and generally watching every move James made, hanging on his every word.

"Sh, Sh," James, would say.

"Do you hear that bird, Alan? That's a bullfinch. Listen."

"Look I see him. He's over there."

On the really hot days they went up beyond the back field to get ice-cold water in the well. Exploring everything, listening for crickets, spotting butterflies on the way. The well was half hidden under a huge flat stone, surrounded by ferns. James held Alan tightly and let him stretch out flat on his belly against the damp cold earth to scoop out the icy water. A special friendship and trust grew between the two of them. An unlikely pair. The young and the old, both in their wellingtons.

By now Alan had acquired an old cap belonging to James. It was too big for him but he loved it. It kept the sun out of his eyes and he felt more like a farmer. Sometimes, in the evenings Alan would call into James and watch him tie flies for fishing. Hair, feathers, wax, varnish and pliers all spread out on a newspaper on the kitchen table. James's failing eyesight was not a hindrance – he could tie flies with his eyes shut. Alan's favourite was a pheasant-tail nymph tied from the feather of a cock pheasant.

On very special balmy warm evenings, Alan's mother let him stay up late. James would pack a flask and sandwiches into the fishing bag and take a big torch from the top of the dresser and they'd head off to a sheltered spot on the edge of the river. Their "lucky" spot. One evening Alan unravelled the line as James attached the fly. James wielded the rod like a whip and the fly came alive, hopping on the water, making little circles along the river. Almost immediately he was rewarded with a hefty trout. Young Alan could hardly contain himself; he helped with the landing and weighing. Ignoring the midges as they landed on his appetizing, juicy skin. He never flinched, absorbed in the magic of the river by torchlight. James's leathered skin was immune to the insects.

They fished, neither talking, both comfortable in each other's company. Always. The repair work continued during the day and Alan's mother made bright curtains and cushions. In no time at all the whole house was transformed.

Lucy surprised them all by taking her first few steps.

"Time for her to get wellie boots," James said as they all clapped. He was delighted he'd been there when Lucy walked. Lucy was chuffed with herself and the reaction of her audience. She went for encore after encore.

With the house finished, James and Alan turned their hands to the garden, the Godforsaken wilderness. They tackled it in small sections. The first thing on their list was a hutch for Elvis. They built a big run all around it. Alan made a sign "Gracelands" to hang on the outside.

Then they dug a little vegetable patch and planted lettuce, Elvis's favourite. James transplanted clumps of flox and lupins from his own garden into two big flowerbeds on either side of the cottage door.

And all the while the two friends grew closer. The boy stopped talking about his father's busy life and started to enjoy his own. James was never too busy. There were no more lonely times for either of them.

The days grew shorter and the young boy swapped his tee shirt for a jumper. They still headed off on their walks, talking all the time, heads nodding in unison.

"Well lad," James said to Alan one day when winter had definitely moved in and the smell of turf knitted into their clothes, "you've done well. You've done a great job with the cottage. All the mending and fixing are finished now. I bet your mam's right proud of you now the fixing's all done."

"Oh, she is Mister, I heard her tell my nana on the phone. She told Nana all about it and all about you and all about my fishing and guess what? Nana's coming down to stay for a while."

"Oh, she'll get a right surprise when she sees all the fixing you've done, Alan."

"Yeah, I'm glad she's coming, she's the one who bought Elvis for me. She even gave him his name, after her favourite singer. She's always singing, especially Elvis songs. She even grabs me and does funny dances. She's real funny."

"I can't wait to meet her. She sounds like just what this place needs."

"You know you're wrong about all the fixing being done, Mister. It's not all done yet. My mam has another bit of fixing planned. I heard her talking to my Nana. I heard her tell Nana that she was going to fix her up with the lovely fella next door."

And then Alan gently slipped his soft little hand into James's and the only sound to be heard, as the two pals trundled off down the lane, was the clump, clumping of their wellington boots and a very loud guffaw from James.

Maeve Binchy's books include *Circle of Friends, Light a Penny Candle, Echoes, Silver Wedding, Dublin 4, The Glass Lake, Evening Class, The Copper Beech, The Lilac Bus, Tara Road, Victoria Line, Central Line, Firefly Summer, Nights of Rain and Stars, This Year It Will Be Different, Quentins* and *Whitethorn Woods.*

www.maevebinchy.com

16. THE COUNSELLOR CAT
Maeve Binchy

Sheelagh wanted to be a counsellor from the very start. She was good with people, she could feel their pain and anxiety. She could sympathise enough to be of help but not too much in case they would be overcome by self pity.

In theory she should have trained as a psychologist and worked in a busy city practice. But this wasn't possible for Sheelagh because she was a cat. And they are prejudiced about letting cats enrol in Third Level Education. So she was philosophical about it. Do what you can from where you are. You can't fight blind prejudice. You're never going to get them to believe that cats can understand every word THEY say. The problem is that they have faulty hearing and only hear meows and yelps and purrs, instead of very sophisticated language. From her first day on earth Sheelagh knew it was going to be an uphill struggle.

She was born in a garden shed. Her mother had told her that All was Not Well in the big house and better to stay well clear of them at the moment. The Man had come home early from his work and found the Woman in bed with the gardener. Instead of being pleased that everyone was having a nice lie down, he had lost his temper and started to hit the gardener with the leg of a chair.

Sheelagh's mother had arrived in the door looking for a nice warm quiet place to give birth to the kittens, but had taken in the situation at a glance and gone speedily back out to the shed.

When Sheelagh was a few days old and able to take everything in, she asked her mother what all the shouting was about.

"Humans are very odd" her mother explained. "They go completely mad over the simple business of mating. Instead of just getting on with it like we do, they have a whole series of rules and regulations about who can and who can't with whom. No wonder they are always getting confused."

Sheelagh's mother sighed over the silliness of it all, and when the kittens were about two weeks old she started bringing Sheelagh and her brothers one by one into the Big House where they lived, or thought that they lived.

And the Man was furious and aimed a kick at her. "Another alley cat," he shouted at Sheelagh's mother.

Sheelagh's mother went to the Woman for consolation but there wasn't much help to be found there either. "Better go your own way, Puss Cat, we're all for the high jump at this point. Get yourself a good lawyer if you know what's good for you, you and that scrawny lump of black and white fur in your mouth," and then she burst out crying again.

Sheelagh didn't like being referred to as a scrawny lump of black and white fur especially as her mother had told her she was quite beautiful, but she didn't have much time to brood about it. The Man who was in a terrible temper, picked her up off the ground and ran outside with her. Then he put her in a dustbin and placed the lid on before shouting at Sheelagh's mother to get the hell out of here if she knew what was good for her.

Poor Sheelagh was very frightened as she sat in the dustbin waiting to be rescued. She could hear her mother passing by shouting to her, begging her to indicate her whereabouts. But Sheelagh was too small and too weak to move, and eventually she heard her mother's voice go further and further away.

Ages later big shouting men came to empty the bin and Sheelagh was pitched into a huge truck. One of the bin men saw her. "Aren't people cruel?" he said and put her inside his jacket. Sheelagh begged him to tell her mother that she was safe but he couldn't understand a single word she said. So she went home with him to his girlfriend.

Sheelagh knew the timing wasn't right. The girlfriend was expecting kittens or baby humans of her own. Anyway, she was going to have some sort of a litter, and wasn't particularly interested in a scrawny ball of fur.

The dustman, who was called Jimbo, was slow at understanding this, but he kindly brought Sheelagh up to a Cat Protection place where she heard terrible stories about other cats. Hearing them made her own adventure seem almost insignificant.

At least she had met a nice bin man, and if his mate were not about to produce her own litter, he probably would have kept her. Why couldn't he ask his litter if they'd like me when they're born? Sheelagh wanted to know. But apparently human kittens don't know anything for ages so there's no point really in talking to them.

Sheelagh went to Mrs Murphy, a very kind old lady, who gave her saucers full of cream which was nice but a bit indigestible. Personally she would have preferred more iron and vitamins. The old lady developed a bad cough and nobody understood when Sheelagh ran up and down the road telling people that she was in bad shape. Eventually Sheelagh sat on the doorstep howling until neighbours came in to see what was amiss.

They all congratulated Sheelagh on alerting them, but it turned out that the vet, or the human vet whatever they call them said that Mrs Murphy had to go and live in a home for elderly humans and Sheelagh couldn't go with her. She cried when she said goodbye.

"You're a very wise little cat, Sheelagh, never forget that," Mrs Murphy said with tears in her eyes.

Sheelagh explained that she knew she had been given lots of brains and understanding but she was very pissed off that nobody except other cats seemed to understand her. And Mrs Murphy stroked her head and said the next person to get her would be a very lucky person. But it wasn't a lucky person, it was a howling drunk.

Sheelagh knew that because it was what the neighbours called him.

"Frank is nothing but a howling drunk," they said to each other about him.

He was very forgetful. He forgot to have his own meals and to get any for Sheelagh. He once said it was a pity she couldn't just drink a pint like somebody normal, and Sheelagh said she was perfectly happy to drink a pint with him to be sociable, but the pub wouldn't let her sit up on a high stool and drink out of a tankard and, besides, she DID need some food as well, even if he didn't. But as usual he never understood a word.

So she blew the whistle on him, and when his mother came round to visit, Shelagh went and opened the cupboard where he hid all the empties so that his mother realised exactly how much of a howling drunk he had become.

But it all worked out badly because he was sent off to a home for drunken humans and Sheelagh was back again in the Cat Protection place. So far Sheelagh had got Mrs Murphy into a nursing home, and Frank into an alcoholics' place. She realised that she was a cat of great power.

Next time she got a nice middle-aged couple who had never owned a cat before. She wondered what she could do to help them along in their lives. She studied them carefully.

The man wrote children's stories, was kindly and he often practiced his golf swings in the garden. He was quite good but he said he was having trouble with his follow through. Sheelagh realised that he was holding his club too tightly. She told him this but as usual he thought she was just meowing aimlessly.

The woman wrote stories for bigger people. They seemed reasonably together, for humans that is. They didn't fight with each other about mating with the wrong people like the first couple had. They didn't get feeble and sick like Mrs Murphy had. They certainly liked their wine but weren't howling drunks like Frank. But they did FUSS a bit too much. They got upset when work had to be finished in time, when they got bad reviews, when planes were late or traffic was bad. So Sheelagh taught them how to relax. She lay down and stretched and stretched and then went to sleep with paws outstretched. And soon they got the idea.

"I wish we were more like Sheelagh," the man writer said once.

"Of course she has nothing going on in her furry little head," the woman writer said

As if, Sheelagh thought.

There she was a cat counsellor in a confused world, where no one spoke her language and this woman writer thought she had nothing going on in her head. So Sheelagh just rolled over and over beside the laptop computer, four paws in the air and a smile of pure pleasure on her face until finally the stupid writers got the message, put the lids on their machines and went to open a bottle of wine and relax.

Mission accomplished Sheelagh, she said to herself happily.

Catherine Daly's books include *All Shook Up*, *Charlotte's Way*, and *A French Affair*. She is the moderator of the popular website www.writeon-irishgirls.com.

www.catherinedaly.com

17. NOT THIS TIME, JOSEPHINE!
Catherine Daly

"Don't look at me like that," Sally warned. "It's not going to do you any good. You're not sleeping on the sofa – you have a perfectly good basket in the kitchen."

At the word 'basket', the Pug lifted her aristocratic little snout into the air, turned her head away from Sally, and wriggled her hind quarters to settle herself more securely into the brocade cushion.

"Down, Josephine," Sally warned. "Down, now! I mean it."

Sally closed her laptop to show that she meant business and stood up. Then she walked slowly towards the sofa to give Josephine a chance to get down. But Josephine was sulking, and as soon as she was lifted she let her limbs go limp, forcing her reluctant new owner to pick her up in both arms and transport her unceremoniously to the kitchen where she deposited the little dog in her 'basket'.

Although 'basket' was somewhat of a misnomer, Josephine's bed might more accurately be described as a canine boudoir. It consisted of a large purple, kidney-shaped beanbag, with a dimple in the middle for Josephine to snuggle into. It was covered in the plushest, softest velvet Sally had ever felt and 'scattered' at either end were two shocking-pink, faux-fur cushions.

Josephine had come to live with Sally (to say that Sally had come into possession of Josephine would misrepresent the hierarchy of their relationship) after Sally's aunt Margaret went into hospital. Margaret, a spinster aunt by profession, had owned no less than eight Pugs down through the years, of which Josephine was by far the most outrageous.

"Don't worry, she'll settle down in no time," Margaret had reassured her niece by phone. "Before long you'll wonder what you ever did without her. She'll be a bit of company for you. Give you something other than work to think about."

Sally knew her aunt disapproved of her solitary existence. Divorced, and with no children to show for her seven year marriage, her aunt's assertion that she must lead a very 'lonely' life began, as the years passed, to sound as though she meant 'selfish'. But having been badly burnt in the relationship stakes, Sally was reluctant to try again. In a lot of ways, she, Margaret and Josephine were alike. Surviving very nicely without a member of the opposite sex, thank you very much.

The phone rang as Sally sat back down at her desk.

"Did you call him?" her aunt asked with very little preamble. "The man the vet recommended, did you call him?"

Sally held back her sigh. "Not yet Margaret, no. I haven't had a chance."

"Well you should," her aunt tutted. "There's no point in complaining that Josephine isn't adapting to her new life, if you won't do one simple thing to help accommodate her."

Sally thought of her cancelled holiday (it would be too upsetting for Josephine to be abandoned again so soon), the rearrangement of her small apartment, the morning and evening walks, the getting up to go out whenever Josephine whined and scratched at the door, and the introduction of meat to her vegetarian fridge. She wondered how many more 'one simple thing' she would need to do. She thought of phoning a few nursing homes in the hopes of finding one which would accept pets, instead of the expensive one her aunt had chosen to be with two of her closest friends. But the thought disappeared as soon as it appeared. Aunt Margaret had been like a second mother to Sally, who was the eldest of seven children. Her own mother had always seemed to be either pregnant or nursing an infant sibling throughout Sally's childhood. If it hadn't been for Aunt Margaret, Sally would never have gone to university and would never have been able to set up her own web-business. If it hadn't been for Aunt Margaret, Sally wouldn't own a luxurious apartment for Josephine to move into with her.

"I'll ring him today," she promised. The silence at the other end of the phone was disconcerting. "Now, straight away," she offered. "That is, as soon as you've finished giving me your news."

Sally played with a vellum business card while her aunt filled her in on gossip from the nursing home. Toby Fairweather. The name was in bold black print, followed by a series of intimidating letters, which declared Toby to be a bona fide veterinary surgeon. Small animal specialist, the card claimed. Sally snorted. It was far from 'small' Josephine would be if she continued to eat chicken liver and chocolate at the rate she was scoffing it. Animal behaviourist indeed.

What was an animal behaviourist anyway? Sally wondered. It all sounded a bit 'Californian' especially as when the first time she rang the number, a squeaky-voiced receptionist asked whether she would be looking for an individual or group session.

"A group class, I mean," the voice had gone on to clarify. "You know, owners and dogs meet in the park and learn things like 'Sit!', 'Fetch!', 'Walkies!'."

But the explanation had come too late for Sally who was finding it hard to banish the vision of assorted pooches sitting on beanbags, discussing puppy separation anxiety and 'issues' with their various owners. She had hung up without making any further enquiry. But now that she had finally got her phone back, she rang and booked an appointment. A solo session. Or rather a session for just her and Josephine. Did that count as couples counselling?

A week later, Sally left Toby's surgery in a bit of a daze after a highly embarrassing first session. Josephine hadn't liked being pointed at by a strange man and had bitten Dr Fairweather.

"What on earth has got into you . . . you . . . you . . . dog?" an agitated Sally asked Josephine, as she followed her dog who was tugging at her lead to get away from the vet's practice as fast as she could.

What had got into Josephine was the shock of being seriously challenged for the first time in her life. Usually a bark, a snarl, or at worst a snap was enough to see off strangers who came too close to Sally, or previously Aunt Margaret. And you might have assumed that Josephine was protecting her owner when she stood between Sally and the vet. Josephine had been simply staking a claim to her exclusive property.

The words, 'you've got to show her you're in charge,' accompanied by a pointed finger and a stern command to

'Sit!' had resulted in the little dog levitating three feet into the air to clamp her jaws onto Dr Fairweather's finger.

Sally tried to look like she was in charge now. At a safe distance from the surgery, Josephine sniffed at a tree, waddled and spread her legs to indicate that she was about to perform her daily ritual, so Sally tried to make believe that it was all part of her plan.

"Good girl," she encouraged. "At the edge of the pavement, like I told you. That's it. Good girl!"

Josephine ignored her. Sally pulled a plastic bag out of her pocket and scooped up the little offering while Josephine watched the world go by, yapping once or twice to exchange gossip with other passing pooches. When her human companion had completely finished, dropped her package in the bin and wiped her hands on a wet-wipe, Josephine barked amiably to acknowledge her again. She pulled gently on her lead, to indicate she wanted to get going again.

"Of course," Sally muttered darkly. "Dr Fairweather wants me to show her who's boss, does he? I'd like to see him pretend he's in charge while he's scooping poop."

Maybe she just wanted to prove Toby Fairweather wrong, but over the next few months Sally spent more and more time with him, and he and Josephine settled into an uneasy truce. The little dog pretended to be deaf to any over-outrageous command (like, for example, to get down off Sally's lap and sleep in the cold kitchen), while the vet learned to pick his battles.

Several months later, when Sally and Toby received their first joint party invitation, she realised that they had officially entered the state of coupledom. And to her surprise it was a more pleasant place to be than she had expected.

She couldn't remember quite how the topic had come up

– probably around the time they were talking about getting married – that Toby told Sally he didn't mind the fact that she couldn't have children. And when she told him that her first husband had left her less than a week after her first fertility treatment, Toby commented at how selfish he'd been.

"Congratulations, dear," her aunt Margaret said when she heard the news about the wedding. "About time too. Now you can stop pretending to need a doggy shrink for Josephine. I don't know why you ever thought you'd ever be able to change her behaviour. Have you never heard the one about old dogs and new tricks?"

"Margaret!" Sally interrupted, "I never suggested it . . . that was you."

"It was me who what dear?"

"Nothing," Sally sighed, conceding defeat. "I suppose you know Toby's got a Pug too? A male? He's only a year younger than Josephine."

"Really? Has he? Come to think of it, I think somebody did mention it once. Such a shame he's got a silly name like Wellington though, isn't it?"

Yvonne Kinsella is assistant producer on the Seoige and O'Shea Show.

18. LOVE – DOGGIE STYLE
Yvonne Kinsella

Meg woke on Sunday morning, as she did most mornings, to a lump of white fluff with razor sharp nails pouncing on her chest and nearly winding her. The only male in her life willing to jump on her every day was Jake, her big furry Samoyed who, at six years of age, still thought he was a baby. Nearly every morning for the last three years or so he dashed into the bedroom and made his presence known by barking loudly and pulling at the duvet. And every morning she dutifully crawled out of bed, led him into the kitchen, fed him and then lazily undressed and threw on a crumpled tracksuit.

She always seemed to find at least one pair of comfy trackie bottoms flung on the bedroom floor amongst the dirty socks and smelly sneakers.

Meg knew herself that being untidy was probably her biggest fault. She often boasted to people, albeit in an embarrassed way after a few drinks, about how she managed to wear the same pair of smelly striped socks for at least three days before even noticing a pong. It was the one thing her mother was always lecturing her about – to not be 'a lazy bitch'.

Trying to hold her head together after a bad night's

drinking session, she pulled on a blue velour tracksuit, tied her dishevelled brown hair up in a scrunchie, pulled on her infamous smelly striped socks and her rather mucky Nike runners (because they were the most comfortable!) and was pulled out the door by Jake who had decided, by barking loudly, that she hadn't time for breakfast before their stroll.

She often thought, mid walk, once the air had circulated through her head and she had woken a little, just how lucky she was to have such a fantastic amenity right on her doorstep. She lived in Carpenterstown, a mere 10 minutes stroll to the famous Dublin park that housed the palatial dwelling of Aras an Uachtarain, the home of the President of Ireland and the house of the American ambassador – two stately dwellings that she could only imagine were fantastic in the inside as well as out.

She loved to walk past both houses every morning and just imagine what life must be like for the 'other half'.

But this morning in particular, despite having no make-up on and recovering from a major hangover, having knocked back at least three bottles of wine the night before, she felt fresh and breezy and her worries seemed to have dissolved. It's amazing, she thought, how after a few minutes walk in the sunshine a hangover can seem to disappear. The sunglasses of course helped a bit.

Jake was pulling her through the high grass as always, wanting her to throw a plastic bottle he had plucked up from a nearby hedge so he could dash after it and mess about. He was a very strong dog, his breed originally came from the arctic area of northern Russia and she often felt as though he truly believed she was a sleigh and it was his God given right to pull her around – like most of the males in her life, she often mused.

She had just come out of a very turbulent two year affair – and that was exactly what it was – an affair.

The guy in question was seven years older than her, and at 25 she felt he had aged her in the two years to feel just as old as him (a greying 32).

He was married with twins, aged nine and as is the case with most illicit affairs involving a married man, he claimed he was 'caught' by the girlfriend when they were in their early twenties and had to marry her because she fell pregnant. Of course he didn't love her and they lived in separate rooms, never had sex and were only together for the kids – yeah, yeah, yeah!

Anyway, after living for so long in the hope that he would actually leave 'the wicked witch' and having tagged along building the imaginary life that lay ahead of them in her head, but knowing all along deep down that it would never happen, she finally decided enough was enough and walked away.

It had been hard, and still was, but she was getting there, ignoring his calls, the rings on the doorbell and the pleading messages on her answering machine at work.

Everyone there knew the scenario and had been great and nobody had made her feel like a bitch for trying to break up a marriage. Deep inside though she felt that way herself. But she had fallen in love with the wrong person, that was all it was, she had convinced herself from day one. It happened to thousands of people all around the world every year – it's life, she thought.

As she walked in the park today, straining to hold onto Jake till she reached the wide field near the Chapelizod gate where she could unleash him on the poor squirrels, who would automatically dash up the nearest tree, she remembered the strolls she would have hand in hand with Kieran every Tuesday and Thursday evening in the park.

He loved Jake and Jake thought he just was another 'puppy' to play with. They would roll around in the grass and Jakey would slobber all over him. She lived for the two evenings when he had to do 'a computer course' in work – giving him at least three hours to have sex, shower and go for a walk with his lover and her dog. It was like something from a film, she often thought. And just like a film it wasn't real and she finally realised it could never be real.

He spent every weekend at home with the kids and 'her'. They went on holidays regularly – just for the kids' sake of course and the only times she got to talk to him was when the wife went out for shopping on Saturday mornings. And even then it was a whispered conversation from his bedroom so the kids couldn't hear. But she spotted him in Dundrum shopping centre on a Saturday afternoon six weeks ago walking hand in hand with the wife and that was it. She felt sick to the pit of her stomach and it just confirmed her worst fears – they weren't 'estranged' as he always argued. He was just like every other sleaze bag who started an affair for the excitement of sex with someone else, the forbidden fruit. He never saw her that day, but when he rang on Monday afternoon to arrange to meet up she let him have it. They argued non-stop for four days, her texting him, and him ringing back screaming at her that it 'wasn't how it seemed'.

But enough was enough for Meg. Looking back on those two years now it all seemed so seedy and she swore it would never happen again. As she breathlessly tried to hold onto Jakey, he suddenly spotted a Jack Russell playfully pulling at his owner's legs fifteen feet away and suddenly made a dart for the poor mutt. Meg screamed at him to stop but he was just determined to get to him, panting and drooling as he dashed towards the spotted pup. Meg suddenly realised that it wasn't the dog he was after but a rubber bone that the brown and white 'JR' had dropped on the grass to go and play with his owner. She raced with him trying to pull him back by tugging at the lead when suddenly the playful dog's owner turned around to see what the commotion was all about. Meg shouted 'I'm sorry' as she continued to pull at Jake.

The man, who was very attractive and looked like a rugby player, broad-shouldered and tanned skin, laughed and picked up the pup. As Jake reached the bone he grabbed it and started to run around in circles. Meg apologised profoundly to the dog owner who just smiled and said, 'I know what it's like'. He had the most amazing sultry brown eyes. He seemed 'perfect' if that's a way to describe a guy.

He just oozed sex and she found herself smiling back repeating over and over again how sorry she was. Jake was totally oblivious to the sexual chemistry he had succeeded in generating between the two dog lovers. He sat down on the ground quietly and started biting away at the rubber bone. Meg said again, "I'm really sorry." And raising her voice she shouted, "Jake, put it down, BOLD!"

The stranger put out his hand and she noticed he had no wedding ring on his left hand. A weird observation she thought, having just met the guy. But there seemed to be some sort of connection, she could feel it. Her stomach was slightly weird, dare she say it, like butterflies fluttering around. The stupid feeling you get when you're a teenager, she thought. Shaking hands with her, he laughed: "I'm Joe. Is he always this frisky?"

"Always," she lied. Actually, it wasn't at all normal for Jake to dash off at the sight of a rubber bone – he had four of them in the back garden and was obviously just bored with his own brands. Fate, she thought. It has to be fate. Joe put his dog on a lead. "This is Lady," he said, "and who have we here?"

"Oh, this is Jake."

"I gathered that," he laughed, "you screamed his name enough times."

"Oh, sorry," she said again feeling all flustered.

"I meant you. I've seen you a few times in the park with your husband, I think?"

"Oh no, she said really quickly. "He's a friend. We just go for walks every now and then, nothing in it. I'm single." She realised just how stupid that sounded as soon as she stopped. But he had seen her before. He noticed her before. OH GOD! And she had never noticed him, how was that? He was gorgeous. It was obviously because all of her precious moments in the park centred around the man she wanted but couldn't have – Kieran O'Shea. Yet here was this hunk who had been watching her and she never noticed. It's true when they say love is blind – or is it that it just makes you blind to everything else around you? She felt herself blush and thought he must be with someone. She said really quickly, "Oh, I think I saw you before as well. Were you with a blonde girl a few weeks ago?'

She hadn't seen him at all but it sounded good and she wanted to find out if he was attached.

"No that wasn't me I'm afraid. I'm like yourself – young free and single."

They both laughed nervously. The dogs started playfully

tugging at the bone on the ground between them. They were barking and the pup was climbing on Jake's back. It looked hilarious. "Lady," shouted Joe, "get off Jake's back. You're very forward, at least wait until the second date."

Meg giggled. "Women!" she said, "there's just no holding some of them back."

After she said it she realised she was being very open and jovial with someone she didn't even know. He could be a mass murderer – he had seen her before – maybe he was a weirdo who stalked young women with dogs? But she knew he wasn't. He looked so gorgeous.

His teeth were the whitest she had seen. He had a light cream puff jacket on and faded jeans with Caterpillar boots. His hair was light brown with blonde bits and he was just so charming. She was dying to see what lay beneath the jacket – plenty of muscles she thought before realising that she was actually staring at him in awe. Talk about playing it cool!

"Do you live near?" he asked.

"Just up the road really. And you?"

"I live about 10 minutes away – it's great for coming down here and just getting away from it all. Lady loves it. I only have her about three months now. I found her straying on the roadside near the local shops and she seemed to take a shine to me. She followed me home and I gave her some food and water and she just seemed to make my house her home. I did put an ad in the Spar window and secretly I was hoping I wouldn't get a call and that was that really – obviously I didn't and the rest as they say is history. I'll be honest, if I had been buying a dog I wouldn't have gone for a Jack Russell – I'm more of a German Shepherd guy myself, but I can't help falling for a damsel in distress – I couldn't have left her there. And as you can see, we're very close now. A bit of a joke with the lads in the pub though – they don't think it's a very macho image – a small mutt. They joke that it mirrors the size of my manhood."

Meg giggled like a little schoolgirl once again. "Well, I think she's gorgeous, and if they have to have a big dog to prove their masculinity, then that's a bit sad."

Meg didn't want to go into the whole story of how she got to own Jake, it sounded mad and a bit 'twee', but it was a similar scenario. She had wanted a dog for ages and decided to visit the local pound. It was heartbreaking looking at all of the gorgeous dogs, big and small, literally staring out of the cages begging her with pleading eyes to take them home.

When she spotted Jakey, who was three years old and had been found roaming along the canal, she immediately fell in love, and he was jumping up and down and twisting around as if he knew her forever and wanted to get out to play. It was definitely love at first sight and he was definitely the love of her life, especially right now.

Joe started to walk with Meg, and as the dogs juggled the now well-gnawed bone around them, both of them had to keep jumping to avoid being mown down by the mutts as they frolicked.

Joe said, "I'll have to head off now, I've a project to finish for work by Tuesday and if I don't get back into it I'm doomed. I brought Lady out just to get a breath of fresh air. What way are you walking home? I'm up by Carpenterstown."

"So am I," Meg said quickly. She couldn't believe this. He was a neighbour, well he must be. If he lived in Carpenterstown he couldn't live too far from her as it was a small enough area.

"That's great," said Joe. "Gives us more time for a chat and these two seem to be getting on grand as well," he added looking down at Jake and Lady who were still messing with each other as they tugged along the old country road just outside the park.

"This probably sounds a bit forward," said Joe "but seeing as though the 'kids' are getting on so well, would you fancy going for a cup of coffee later? You don't have to and don't feel like I'm pushing you into something. I'm really not, just if you're around later I'd love to meet up for a chat – minus the mutts!"

The two dogs barked loudly and pulled at each other's ears as they strolled along up the back road into Carpenterstown. The sun was really strong in the sky and a light breeze was blowing through the trees.

Meg tried to be calm. "I suppose the Carpenter pub would be handy for a cuppa. Where exactly are you living?"

"Riverwood," he said. "And you?

"Riverwood," she laughed, "but I'm not bringing you home. I can't believe we're in the same estate."

"Well, that's fate," he said staring at her with his big brown eyes.

"Must be," said Meg, still in shock at her luck.

"I think the saying 'Lady Luck' must have some truth to it. I'll have to tell the lads a little dog does great things for your macho magnetism. They'll all want one. And I don't feel a bit inferior about your dog being bigger than mine," he laughed.

"Well, as they say, size doesn't matter," said Meg.

He grinned. "We should take this conversation a step further later over a glass of wine instead of a coffee. How does 3:00pm suit?"

"Great," she said. "Sure we can bring the 'kids' home a doggie bag each, at least they wont feel left out then," she smiled. The pair walked on suddenly quiet and in a way a little embarrassed, until they reached the gate leading into their estate. Joe went to the left and Meg turned right into the Chase. They waved and Joe shouted, "threeish?"

"Brilliant," she smiled back and immediately started wondering what she should wear.

Hurrying home, she contemplated her good luck. She had Jake's mad fetish for rubber bones to thank for the chance encounter. Maybe now she could finally move on.

Sarah McInerney is a *Sunday Tribune* reporter.

19. HITCH

Sarah McInerney

A row of white-washed cottages sat sleepily in the dawn, their occupants snug in bed. Except for Josephine Banks. She hopped on one high heel down the tiled hallway, bag, umbrella, coat, keys and phone growing like weeds from various parts of her body. She bit into an apple, and held it in her mouth, fastening the strap on her other shoe and struggling with the wrought iron deadbolt that promised her safety. Up earlier than everyone else, Josephine was still in a hurry.

Flinging open the door, she squinted into the morning sun, and grabbed the wreath of flowers that sat on the hall table, sucking water from a punctured green oasis. She plucked at a curling brown petal that hung from one of the lillies, shut the door behind her, turned, and tripped on her own haste and carelessness. Her apple took flight. Her body surrendered to gravity. Her hands were too busy saving the flowers to be of any help.

She hit the ground head first. A headache burst into life, streaming down the back of her skull to sympathise with the shooting pain in her neck. Cheek scratched against gravel. Curses flowed. She lay there. Aching. Hurt. And wondering if any of the neighbours saw. Two doors down,

McKenzie's curtains twitched. More curses. Her skirt rode high on her thigh, a ladder racing up her new stockings. A patch of blood blossomed on her knee. She pushed herself upright, straightened her skirt, and kicked her apple under a bush. For the birds. Blood pooled in the sole of her shoe. Sticky and warm. She looked at her car and looked at her door. She walked to her car. No time for changing clothes. Sliding into her little red mini, Josephine located a packet of tissues and a box of painkillers from her glove compartment. Using the tissues to stop the blood flow, she threw three white tablets into her mouth and swallowed them dry. Grimacing. Turning the ignition. Trying to ignore the reflex to gag. She reversed the car. And hit something. She felt the reverberations just before she heard a surprised grunt. Trickles of foreboding ran over her body as she peered in the rear view mirror. A perfectly manicured lawn sparkled in front of a perfectly manicured house. Slowly pushing the door open, she peeked around to the back of the car. A pair of army boots protruded from behind the back wheel.

"Jesus Christ." She got out.

A man was lying behind the car. Pale. Unconscious. A puppy sat beside an upended cardboard box, bathing the man's face in saliva. He paused just long enough to look up at Josephine, brown eyes accusing. Josephine took out her phone and called an ambulance. She slid down the side of the car. Her legs didn't want to hold her up. Her mind did somersaults. What would she say? She didn't know the man. She looked like she'd done ten rounds in a boxing ring. It didn't look good. What about the dog? What would she say? What would they think? This couldn't be happening. Not now.

The puppy sat beside the man's head. Whining. Unhappy. Josphine glared at him. Ignored him. Through the morning calm, she heard the faint song of the siren. What would she say? She glanced at McKenzie's. No twitching at the window. Eating breakfast now probably. She could smell the frying fat. Good. She let her hands roam the man's chest, searching through the folds of his faded black t-shirt for something, anything to identify him. She moved to his pockets, front and back. His body was thin. Bones poked at her searching fingers. Sharp in their defence.

The siren was louder now. They'd love the siren. They'd open the curtains and take out their rubbish, and pull out the weeds that had grown unmolested all winter. Then they'd linger and watch and talk and whisper.

Her search grew more frantic. His coat. On the ground. Her fingers were nimble. They closed around a thin, brown leather wallet. One twenty euro note. A few coppers. A video club card. A library card. An old student card. His name. His age. Enough to keep the ambulance men happy. The wallet went back. The ambulance skidded to a halt, all lights and sound and glory. The first of the neighbours appeared. Rolling the lawn mower ahead of him. The paramedics landed on the ground. Clump. They shuffled over, strangely slow in their haste.

"His name is Milo Marks," Josephine said, stepping back. "He's 33. He was behind the car. I didn't see him. I think he was bending, running after the dog."

Across the street a front door slammed. The O'Donoghues were taking their cat for a walk. The cat dragged at the leash, unaccustomed to such treatment. The O'Donoghues started walking in a circle around their garden. They picked at a few dandelions.

The first paramedic felt for a pulse. He nodded. He pulled up Milo's eyelids, smudging the black eye-liner that resided there. The man was wearing make-up. Josephine tried to take an interest in this, and failed. She sighed and folded her arms and looked at her watch and tapped her foot. The second paramedic looked at her curiously. Her foot froze, mid-tap.

Milo coughed. Squeezed his eyes shut. Squeezed them open. Looked at the paramedic. Screamed. Sat straight up. Paused. He looked at Josephine and smiled sleepily. "Hello. Sorry. Your boot was open."

He lay down again.

The paramedics looked at each other, nodded, and lifted Milo onto the stretcher. Milo sat up again. "Oh, there's really no need for that, thank you. You may leave me down. I'm perfectly alright."

They ignored him. Milo disappeared into the back of the ambulance, his protests muffled from inside the metal box. The second paramedic came back to talk to Josephine. "Are you alright yourself?"

He looked pointedly at her knee. At the blood caked in a river down her leg. At the torn stocking and the red lump on her cheek that promised a purple bruise. Josephine felt the urge to explain. This was no domestic row. "I don't even know him."

The paramedic nodded grimly. "Sure." He looked at her more closely.

"Wait, you're that Banks woman, aren't you? The one they're all talking about. Hey Jimmy!" he grinned and gestured at his colleague, who already had the engine running. "Look who it is, Jimmy."

Josephine felt a red flush creeping up her neck. Anger and shame combined. "Look, I really don't have time to talk," she said. "What's the situation regarding paperwork, or forms or whatever I need to fill out?"

The paramedic ignored her. "Jimmy are you deaf? Get down here. Look. The one from the papers." He jabbed his index finger in the direction of Josephine.

But Jimmy was busy talking into the radio receiver. Whatever news he heard didn't please him. He beeped the horn and growled something at his partner, his words distorted by the windscreen. He revved the engine impatiently. He made signs with his hands. Jimmy was ready to leave.

"Shit. Gotta go." The paramedic couldn't hide his disappointment. He pointed at the ground, where the puppy was having a heated exchange with his box of straw. "Do we need to call the pound, or is he yours?"

Josephine looked at him. Then down at the puppy. She knelt. "Spot!" She patted the ground beside her. "Here Spot." The puppy ignored her.

"He's mine." She looked up at the paramedic. "He's fine with me."

The paramedic snorted. "Yeah. Right. Very safe, I'm sure." Turning on his heel, he lifted himself into the van without another word. Josephine watched it drive away. The O'Donoghues had given up all pretences. They stood and stared and whispered. Josephine stood up and glared back. Between them the air bristled.

At the end of the street, the ambulance screamed to a stop. All heads turned to look. The back door of the ambulance swung open, and Milo sprung onto the ground. He brushed at his clothes. The paramedics clumped and shuffled over to him. They all shook hands and laughed and patted backs. Guffaws wafted down the street. The best of friends, they said goodbye. The paramedics hurried back to the cab. Milo strolled towards Josephine. Heads spun slowly, following his progress. The cat wailed. The leash was no longer a novelty. The puppy ignored the cat. His straw was more interesting. Josephine ignored the lot of them and walked back to her car. Closed the door. Closed her eyes. Willed the nightmare to end.

White knuckles rapped on the window. Milo smiled at her. "Very sorry to bother you," he said, his voice carrying the trace of an English accent. "I just wanted to apologise for this whole little mess. Your boot, you see" he pointed at the back of the car. "It was open. Something could have fallen out."

He smiled again and shrugged a big expressive shrug that poked his shoulder bones into peaks. One side of his head was red and angry. The paramedics had patched some white gauze to a cut above his eye. Black eyeliner streaked over one cheekbone.

Josephine rolled down the window. "Look, I'm sorry for knocking you down, but I really have to go now. I'm late. If you want to talk about insurance, maybe you could drop by tomorrow evening?"

"Oh no," Milo waved a hand at her. "There's no problem there. It's just a little scratch. But maybe if you're going in the direction of town you could give me a lift?"

His eyebrows wriggled up his forehead hopefully.

"Fine, fine." Josephine knew she sounded ungracious. "Of course, I'd be only too happy. Put the dog in the box, and hop in."

The little red car chugged past silent eyes to the end of the street and finally turned the corner. The whirr of the engine filled the silence. For a while. Until Josephine broke it. "Where am I dropping you?"

"Really, you're very kind. The bus station is fine."

Josephine ran a red light. Cars screamed, horns wailed. Milo yelled, and threw himself over the box on his lap. Josephine drove on. The mini slipped through the intersection to safety.

"No, look, I'll drop you home. Where do you live?"

"Well, that's very nice of you," said Milo, peering up at her from under the crook of his arm. "I live in Thomastown actually. You're sure that's not too far?"

It was. Tucked away on the outskirts of the outskirts, Thomastown was a nightmare of bad traffic, bad roads, and one-way systems. Josephine swallowed, and glanced at the wreath of flowers that had been relegated to the back seat.

"No, of course not, that's fine. Least I can do."

The engine whirred. The puppy moved. Straw rustled. "So what were you doing so far from home anyway?"

She tried to sound casual. Tried not to let the frustration show.

Milo smiled. "Collecting this little fellow." He tapped the cardboard box. "From a chap on your street, actually. He breeds them. Johnny Traynor. Know him?"

"Not really," said Josephine. "Everyone sort of keeps to themselves on my road. It's good. The privacy. I like it that way."

The engine whirred. Josephine felt the effect of the painkillers wear off. An ache on the side of her head. She looked at the glove compartment. Decided to wait until she got water.

"Why did the ambulance men let you out?" she said.

"My Dad. He works at the hospital."

"Oh. Right. Like a doctor, or surgeon, or something?"

"Yes. Like that."

"Should I take this right turn?"

"Actually I believe the next right is the one. I'm not awfully familiar with the route."

"I thought you lived there?"

Milo shrugged. "Only recently."

He started to hum an eighties tune. Off key, persistent. Straw rustled. Josephine turned on the radio. Soccer. The score was 2-1. She twisted the dial. A politician spouting political gospel. She tried again. Tinny music, number one hit, goddamn awful. She grunted. Turned it off. Silence rushed in to fill the vacuum. Milo started to hum again. Josephine cracked.

"So, what do you do for a living, apart from collecting dogs?"

"I'm a doctor."

Josephine ran a red light. The road was quiet. Nobody cared. Milo held the box tighter. She stared at him. "A doctor. Really. A medical doctor?"

She looked at his shaggy black hair. At his scruffy black boots. At his make-up. Milo blushed under her scrutiny. His fingers picked at the cardboard.

He glanced at her. "Yes. A medical doctor." He cleared his throat. "I really am very sorry about all this. Have I made you late for work?"

"Oh." Josephine looked back to the road. "No. I'm. No. It's fine."

"You don't work Mondays, then? What do you do?"

"No. I mean. Yes. I do, normally. I'm just taking some time off."

"Holidays. Fantastic. Going anywhere nice?"

He looked at her wedding finger. There was a band of pale skin. No ring. "No. It's not really a holiday." She bit her lower lip. "You really don't know who I am?"

"Oh. No. Should I?" Milo leaned in for a closer look. "Are you famous? I'm so sorry. I just don't watch much TV or anything . . ."

"Don't worry, no. I'm not. It doesn't matter." She smiled now. It changed her face. She rolled down the window. The scent of grass and cows and countryside whipped and whirled into the car. Strands of hair struggled out of the tightly wound bun at the back of her head.

They flew in wisps around her head. She didn't stop them.

"Can I ask you a personal question?" Josephine had to shout above the wind.

Milo shrugged.

"What's with the make-up?"

He shrugged again. "Just something I'm trying out."

"Are you a Goth or something?"

"I don't know. Maybe. I've read about Goths. I like some of what they say, it just seems to make sense to me, so I thought I'd join them for a while. Today is my first day. I wasn't really sure what I was doing with the black pencil though."

"And what do you think your patients are going to say, when they see you?"

Milo looked out his window. Josephine saw his lips moving, but couldn't hear him. She shut the window. "Sorry, I missed that?"

Milo didn't turn. "I'm not practising at the moment. My wife died two months ago. I'm just taking some time off."

"Oh. I'm so sorry. I didn't know.'

"Of course you didn't."

The engine whirred. And whirred. And whirred.

"My husband died too." Joesphine's voice was small, like

it came from deep inside her body and lost power on the way.

Fields flashed by the window. They drove towards a looming black cloud. The first drops of rain spattered on the windscreen. Milo looked at her. Silence.

"In our house, he died. I came home, and found him. It was all over the news. You really haven't heard of it?"

Milo shook his head. His eyes pushed out sorrow at her. Suddenly she could see a slip of doctor in him.

"It's left at these crossroads," he said without taking his eyes off her.

Josephine hit the indicator. Embarrassed. Wondering how she could have confided in this strange man with his strange hair and eyes and accent.

"That's what the flowers are for?" Milo nodded towards the back seat.

"I like to get there early," said Josephine. "Before anyone else. By nine o'clock, you'd be surprised how many people are in a graveyard."

"And you don't want to see people because they'll recognise you."

Josephine nodded, waiting for the questions, followed by the horror, followed by the revulsion. Milo rewarded her with silence. The puppy moved.

"So you're looking forward to taking care of Spot?" said Joesphine, just to be saying something.

"Spot?" Milo looked at her enquiringly.

"Him." She nodded at his lap.

"Spot?" He looked outraged. "You called him Spot? Really, I mean, really, that's bloody awful. His name is Jack."

He stared out the window, chest huffing indignantly.

"Doesn't even have one discernable spot on his body," he muttered, eyes sliding in Josephine's direction, intent on bestowing a disapproving stare. His wounded sensibilities were further offended to find her in such a state of giggles that she couldn't breathe. Tears ran down her cheeks as she struggled to keep the car in lane. Embracing the laughter. Letting the tension free.

She waved her hand at him, waiting to be able to make words. "Sorry, it's funny," she said, "that you care so much. Sweet. But funny. So sorry. And apologies to Jack."

She rapped on the box, earning yet another glare from Milo. He folded his arms around it.

Houses flashed. Civilisation approached. Josephine ignored the lowered speed limits. School children leapt back onto footpaths, while mothers shook their fists.

"It's left at the next crossroads, please. Thank you." said Milo.

Joesphine hit the indicator.

Minutes later they pulled up outside a regal old mansion with big old trees and a long driveway. "This is me." Milo unsnapped his seatbelt and relaxed his body for the first time since he'd been privy to Joesphine's driving skills. They sat still for a minute. Uncertain. His hand went to the door.

"Thank you so much for the lift. I really do apologise for all the trouble."

He pushed the door open, one leg swinging onto the pavement.

"Wait." Josephine lay her fingers on his arm. "Wait," she said again, softer this time.

"You'll probably notice it now. Seeing that you've met me. You may as well know then."

Her eyes picked over the floor of the mini, focusing on a stray strand of straw that had escaped from Jack.

"My husband was found hanging. From a hook in the ceiling." she said.

Softly now. Cracked and thin and pained.

"They ruled out suicide," she continued, "they say things didn't add up."

She looked at him. Searching for the doctor she'd glimpsed. For the man who'd lost his wife. For the man who didn't need to ask questions. "They think it was me," she said. "They've charged me. My trial is next year. I'm up for murder."

Milo swung his leg back into the car. "I could make tea," he said. "Would you like tea?"

Sarah Ball's novels include *Nine Months, Marry Me* and *Written in the Stars*

www.sarahball.co.uk

20. THE NINE LIVES OF GEORGE BLACK

Sarah Ball

When the information monitor confirmed my flight as delayed, I was almost tempted to see how many pints I could drink before it changed to boarding, but instead I walked over to the newsagents to choose a book. I picked one of the thrillers fanned out in a display and took it back to my seat in the departure area. I read the back cover several times, unable to fathom what it was about, then got stuck rereading the opening lines as my thoughts kept drifting back to George.

I'd been so busy over the past week, helping with arrangements for the wedding, that I'd had little time to dwell on things, and now my mind was playing catch-up. I watched a security guard walk past with a sniffer dog. It was an energetic Labrador, the perfect pet for a guy on his own, and I wondered whether I should get a dog. I imagined running in the park with a faithful dog by my side, but thoughts of George returned and I felt guilty for considering it. It was no good, I conceded, giving up on my book, I was always going to be more of a cat-person.

I was twelve when Mum first introduced me to George. She picked me up from school one day and drove me to a farmhouse somewhere near Epping Forest. She didn't say why we were going there and when we pulled up in the wide, muddy driveway, she turned to me with glassy eyes.

'I know things have been tough for you lately,' she started, and I squirmed in my seat, fearing she might cry. Dad had left only a fortnight earlier and the heavy emotional discussions were getting embarrassingly frequent. Fortunately she just smiled bravely (an expression I suspected she had copied from Angie in *EastEnders*) and said, 'well, I've got a surprise for you. Something I think will cheer our house right up. You want to come and see?'

I nodded. It was easier than telling her I just wanted to go home, that the thought of anything new and different made me feel sick and all I wanted to do was play on my Atari until bedtime. But I humoured her, feigning interest in what I suspected would be something involving soft furnishings or a large garden plant.

When I first saw George he was curled up in a Jacob's Crackers box pushed next to an overflowing bin in a vast and tatty kitchen. The woman who let us in introduced him by saying, 'this one's George. He was the runt of the litter, born with a broken leg. They said he wouldn't make it and he's not been that lively since. I expect you'd prefer one of these . . . ,' she continued steering Mum away from George to see the other kittens that were tearing up and down the hall carpet, claws out, tails up, tumbling over each other in skittish excitement.

Mum looked back at me and said, 'what do you think, Ned? These ones are fun.' But I kept staring at the kitten in the crackers box as he trembled in his sleep.

When Mum drove us home I stared at George, feeling almost like I'd been given a consolation prize. A case of what a shame you've been dealt the parental divorce card; you could have had an enduring father figure and a secure family life, but don't worry, you won't be going home empty-handed. Here's a ginger Tom the size of a tennis ball with a gammy leg and big paws to fill the space in your wounded heart. It was such an obvious gesture that even I, aged twelve and emotionally confused, could smell it a mile off. I wanted to be indifferent and let Mum know that it wasn't as easy as that, but I couldn't help myself. The kitten was injured and alone, a kindred spirit. I understood him, and was confident that when he deigned to open his eyes, he'd see a life long friend in me.

He hadn't shown much promise at first. He was scrawny and sullen with a tendency to pee on a patch of carpet behind the wardrobe. I had faith in him though, and even Mum spotted his potential.

'Honestly Ned,' she said to me once, smiling illusively over her evening gin and tonic, 'he'll be a big one all right. Look at the size of his paws. Feet like that are a good sign, I'm telling you.'

He got bigger and stronger every day, developing a lean physique like the young lions I'd seen on nature programmes. He had green eyes, flecked with gold, and a wide, proud nose that made him look almost gladiatorial. He was also a vocal cat, with a low, repetitive 'meow' that announced his arrival or his need for attention. I'd read somewhere that kittens liked boiled eggs, so every morning I put an egg on the stove for George then let him lick the leftovers of my cereal. Slowly, I started to win him over.

He'd find my lap when I was watching TV or scratch at the door when I was having a bath. During those first few months, Mum's moods were erratic. She was either desperately trying to be my best mate or taking a tumbler of gin up to her bedroom and muttering words like 'treacherous' and 'destitute' into her bedside phone. I would avoid her as much as possible and George helped me do that. He kept me company, preventing me from tuning out the world, and kept my feet warm at night when Mum got thrifty with the central heating. And then, when George was just nine months old, he went missing, and I realised that life without him wasn't worth thinking about.

For fifteen days I walked the streets of North London. My best friend, Alex, made me some flyers on his computer that I could stick to lampposts. MISSING, they read, GEORGE BLACK, MUCH-LOVED FAMILY PET.

After a fortnight of searching, everyone thought it was time to give up. The receptionist at the vets was obviously counting to ten and trying to calm her breathing when she recognised my voice on the line. Mum even offered to get me a dog, insisting that a dog would be more appropriate for a boy my age.

One chilly Sunday evening I sat on our doorstep in my pyjama bottoms, staring down the foggy street with tears in my eyes. I tuned in to the rhythmic sound of distant traffic. Suddenly I perked up when I thought I heard that distinctive 'meow'. It was so far off it could have been just my imagination, but then it came again, louder this time, and I got up, running barefoot down the drive to see George illuminated in the glow of a streetlight. I crouched down, elated and desperate to hold him, but when he reached me he fell through my hands onto the tarmac, his chest heaving.

The vet said he was seriously dehydrated and malnourished. He must have been trapped somewhere, unable to get food or water, and that had he been gone another day he probably would have died. Mum didn't watch TV that night. Instead she made him porridge, called him a 'daft sod' and sat with me in the kitchen, as I made sure he ate up.

Over the following year George seemed determined to prove himself as a cat of worth. He started leaving us gifts on the doorstep. Dead mice would appear every week or so, carefully laid out on the mat. On my fifteenth birthday I was woken to the sounds of Mum screaming in the kitchen before bursting into my room brandishing a sandal. 'A rat! Ned, it's an actual bloody rat, I kicked it when I went to get the milk! For crying out loud, it went on my bare toes!'

I sat up, impressed. 'How big was it?'

She made a wailing noise at that, then stomped off to the bathroom.

Then George decided to up-the-ante and pick a fight with a fox. He couldn't have timed it any worse. I was in the back garden late one night, kissing my first girlfriend Jo. I'd managed to slide my hand up the back of her soft jumper and she didn't seem to be objecting. My other hand was stealthily stroking its way up the uncharted territory of a pencil skirt when there was a sound, rather like the one I would imagine greets you in the burning fires of hell. A frantic caterwauling, a chilling screeching and a long, pained yowl.

Jo, white as a ghost, jumped up and started banging the back door, trying to get away from the noise. I knew it was George, and a minute later he came out of the dark, covered in blood, one eye closed and a tear in his left ear. Jo ditched me after that, unimpressed that I had gone straight to help George and had left her on the doorstep frightened out of her wits.

Then one Saturday morning, my friend Alex and I were
leaving the house to catch an early showing at the cinema.
We got to the end of the drive and were about to turn in
the direction of the bus stop when Alex stopped and stared
up the road saying, 'What the . . . ?'

I followed his eyes and saw a squirrel streaking up the
middle of the road. It flew past us like a hairy dart and
Alex looked at me quizzically. Then I saw George in hot
pursuit, his legs making long strides and his paws thud thud-
ding on the white lines of the road. I called out to him but
he was locked onto his target. Alex shouted, 'Go George,
go!' like we were at Aintree, cheering the riders down the
home straight.

We rushed out into the road as he passed and watched
them reach the T-junction. The squirrel carried straight on,
shooting up a tree and George, who was gaining on him,
was just about to do the same when a car rounded the
corner and braked hard, swerving to avoid him.

We started running towards them but by then the car was
skidding and George had vanished. It was my mum's car, I
realised, as it collided with a low brick wall that slowly
toppled over and crumpled into a garden.

'Mum!' I cried, my heart thumping, 'Mum, are you okay?
Where's George? Have you killed George?'

Mum got out, looking at the wall, then at us, then behind
her. 'Was that George?'

'Did you hit him? Where is he?' I was frantic, then I felt
something rub against my legs and there he was, making
out like nothing had happened.

'You'd better take him as far away from me as possible,
Ned,' Mum warned, her voice low and shaking, 'because
next time, I won't miss.'

Mum got her sense of humour back when it turned out the guy whose wall she'd hit was a recent divorcee called Charles with a converted farmhouse in the Loire Valley and a passing resemblance to Harrison Ford. They went out for dinner and she changed overnight. She got her hair done, started smiling for no reason and filled the bathroom with bottles of time-defying creams. I was happy for her, but it was time for me to move on.

I studied hard to get the grades to make university. I was desperate for a bachelor pad and a student life. My plan was to go to Southampton University and do an English degree. It was near enough to feel like I wasn't abandoning Mum, far enough away that we could have our own lives. And I wanted to get a shared house, so that George could come too.

Surprisingly my best-laid plans didn't go awry and in the autumn of 1994 I was driven down to Southampton with George in a basket on the back seat. I had found a flat in a large house a mile from the town, broken up into ten separate apartments, and quickly fell in love with the girl across the hall.

She was gorgeous. A drama student called Andrea with wispy blonde hair, a willowy body and a cool bohemian flat. It was a doomed obsession that took up most of my student life and turned me into an embarrassingly desperate, jealous wreck. I was even putting George in jeopardy to harness her affections.

One time in that first month, Andrea called me over to her flat to help her tune in her video player. We ended up watching a film, drinking Chianti and kissing on the sofa. George nearly drowned in her fish tank trying to catch a turtle while I tried to fathom the layers of her chiffon top.

After The Kiss I tried to turn my flat into a beatnik den by painting one wall deep purple and putting a red light bulb in the living room lamp. George was not impressed by the paint fumes or by the incense candles I'd left burning by the door (I kept fanning the scent out into the hall so Andrea would notice). He must have climbed out the open window to sit on the window ledge for some fresh air. I didn't realise this until a few hours later when I shut the window and sent George falling two storeys down into the car park below. I raced down the flights of stairs, crying, 'shit, I've killed George!' as I knocked past people with my hands outstretched, hoping to make it outside in time to catch him.

I wasn't quick enough, of course, but when I got to the car park I was amazed to see him sitting, unhurt, on the bonnet of an old Rover Metro. He stared daggers at me before jumping down and stalking away, his tail in the air.

Looking back, he was probably trying to tell me that Andrea was a path to disaster, but I didn't realise until I graduated, and she left for San Francisco with some guy called Flynn.

I trained to be a teacher and got a job at a school in Islington. George came too, of course. I got stuck in a routine of going out most nights and drinking too much. I'd wake up in the night, worried that I was going to end my days alone. That I would turn into one of those men you see staggering about in town centres wearing an old tartan bobble hat and picking fights with lamp posts. I was on a downward spiral that ended up with me punching a neighbour who nearly poisoned George with slug pellets. He was laughing about it in the pub, not bothered in the slightest, and I saw red. The landlord gave me a free drink and a cigar but I still wasn't proud of what I did. I knew it was time to sort myself out.

I bought a lovely old flat near the shops, took up running, and even managed a few short-but-sweet relationships. At twenty-eight I was in better shape than ever before but George was getting old. He stopped leaving mice on my doorstep, despite my flat having a plentiful supply, and instead he stayed indoors, sleeping by the radiator. I knew something was wrong when he started turning down porridge. I took him to the vet, who told me he had feline leukaemia, and two weeks later his journey came to an end.

As I sat in the departure lounge, waiting for my flight, I remembered those times with George. I thought about the times in his life when he'd cheated death, and the one time he hadn't. I counted eight altogether. Eight lives, not the nine a cat was supposed to have. I wondered what other scrapes he'd got into that I didn't know about. There must have been plenty.

We'd been through a lot together. We'd grown up together, and without him my house felt eerily empty. I kept thinking I could hear him meowing and I was still making extra breakfast for his bowl. I needed a change of scenery and the wedding was an ideal opportunity. Mum was finally marrying Charles at his farmhouse near Châteauroux and I was going to look after their house while they honeymooned in Paris.

I got up, stretched and decided to get a bite to eat from the café behind me. I was just putting my book in my rucksack when a voice came over the tannoy.

'Attention please, this is a passenger announcement. Can George Black please come to the information desk? George Black. Thank you.'

I froze, my heart freefalling. George Black? Did I really just hear that? I saw the information desk at the other end of the vast hall, snatched up my bag and started zigzagging through the milling travellers, hurrying towards it. I didn't know what I was expecting to see, but I just couldn't ignore his name. I reached the desk, glancing wildly around but not knowing what I was looking for.

The man behind the desk was already dealing with a woman, passing her some documents. There was nobody else around, nobody was coming. I wondered if perhaps I had imagined it and felt suddenly unsettled. Was I losing the plot completely?

'How long do you think it'll be before the flight to Tours starts boarding?' the woman was asking. That was my flight, I realised, tuning in to their conversation.

'It should hopefully be in the next hour,' he said. 'I'm sorry I can't tell you any more than that yet.'

'OK, thanks.' She moved away from the desk and the man behind it turned to me.

'Can I help you?'

'No, well, yes. Maybe. Did I just hear a message on the tannoy for a George Black?'

'Yes. But that query has been dealt with.' The man looked confused, as though I might also claim to be George Black. 'You're not . . . ?'

'No, no, I'm not. It doesn't matter.' I turned away, disappointed. What had I been expecting? George, my old cat, waiting to bid me farewell?

'It was me,' a voice behind me said.

I turned around to face the woman who had asked about the flight to Tours. She was about my age with long brown curls and the loveliest face I had ever seen.

'I'm George Black,' she said. 'Well, Georgia actually.'

'Oh!'

She was smiling at me with friendly ease. 'You weren't looking for me then?'

'No, er, I just heard the name and . . .' I laughed, feeling ridiculous '. . . it's daft, really.'

She raised her eyebrows and looked at me with amusement, as though she was waiting further explanation.

'Well, that was my cat's name. George Black. I'm Ned Black, you see. It was just weird, hearing it on the tannoy. He only died a week ago.'

I fully expected her to start backing away from me at that point but instead her face melted into a look of sympathy.

'Ah, that's so sad, I'm really sorry. How long did you have him for?'

'Sixteen years.'

'Wow.' She looked off into the distance for a second, as though remembering something, then said, 'well, I can imagine how you feel. My cat died last year and I have to say I'd be pretty spooked if I heard her name over a tannoy like that.'

'What was she called?'

'Erm.' She started blushing. 'Tilly Whiskers.'

We both laughed, the ice now properly broken, and started to chat, comparing notes on why we were flying alone to France. When there was a break in conversation I said, 'listen, seeing as we've both got an hour to spare; you fancy getting a coffee or something?'

She thought for an agonising second. 'OK, why not?'

I grinned at her, unable to believe my luck, then realised how uncool I was looking and helped gather up her belongings instead. As I bent down to pick up her bag I caught sight of her boarding pass, poking out of a pocket. 'How funny,' I muttered.

'What's that?'

'Your name. I still can't believe you're called George Black.'

'I know, it is weird.' She looked at me, her green eyes teasing. 'But then, I always knew I was a cat-person.'

Patricia O'Reilly's books include *Time &*
Destiny, Once Upon a Summer Time,
Felicity's Wedding and *Writing for Success.*

www.patriciaoreilly.net

21. A PERFECT ACCESSORY
Patricia O'Reilly

From the afternoon Cat arrived uninvited, unannounced and unwelcome on the doorstep of her office, Silky Donovan's orderly working life was reduced to chaos. Cat was a singularly unlovely scrap of bedraggled fur with sharp claws, hostile eyes and a penetrating hiss. However for Mandy, Silky's indispensable PA, it was love at first sight. Cat immediately became her priority from that moment on.

Standing at her easel on a cold November morning, immaculate in Gucci trousers, a Rocca polo neck and Jimmy Choo heels, Silky tried to absorb herself in pasting a mock-up of photographs and line-drawings for Caroline Clancy's Career Collection. Caroline was *Plum's* highest profile client, and hotly tipped to receive this year's Business Woman of the Year award.

A quarter to ten now. Still no sign of Mandy. Nothing new about that these days. Over the past weeks Mandy had plenty of reasons for being late. Some were highly imaginative, some were hilariously funny and others were catastrophically sad. All were complicatedly feline related. Tough as she tried to be – and you had to be tough to survive in the lifestyle business – Silky was a soft touch. But she was determined to give Mandy a firm talking-to on this occasion. Enough was enough, she told herself.

Plum was a two-woman communications company, which to function efficiently, required its full complement of staff, minus animal problems. If Mandy couldn't guarantee she'd be sitting at her desk by nine o'clock tomorrow morning, she needn't bother coming in again. On several previous occasions, Silky had rehearsed the appropriate words to perfection, but at the last moment had reneged. But today was different.

At twenty past ten, Mandy arrived flushed, breathless and gushing apologies. 'I'm so sorry. Venus was sick. All over the place. In little puddles. Watery and kinda greenish.' If nodding her auburn curls didn't confirm her statement, the cat puke on her jacket and shirt certainly did.

As Silky's resolution wavered, she gave herself a mental kick. But with Mandy so obviously upset, it would take a heart of stone to follow through her original punishment. Instead, she found herself comforting her PA. 'It's a good sign when cats vomit. Gets whatever's causing the problem out of their system. Self-healing, you know.'

'Oh, do you think so?' In her anxiety Mandy would have grabbed at any ludicrous strand of hope.

'Yes, I'm sure.' They were reflex words to sooth Mandy and to nip her drama in the bud. Silky knew little about cats, though despite herself, she was learning fast. However she didn't want to encourage Mandy to spend the entire morning discussing cat sick.

'Do you think I should ring the vet?'

'Well, why don't you wait until you see how she is this evening?'

'I still have her little cat basket in the car,' Mandy said. But Silky grimaced. This was a cut-throat business. A client such as Caroline Clancy was a window of real opportunity and her endorsement of Plum could open endless doors to future career opportunities. Nothing should compromise that.

'Poor you. Poor puss. It must be a dreadful worry,' Silky said, determined however not to spend any more time discussing Venus. 'But I need you here to deal with the phone and emails. And make an appointment with Caroline. Get her here to look over the storyboard.'

Caroline was so busy that it was difficult to pin her down. An appointment was unlikely to sort out within the next few days.

Forty minutes later, Silky stood back in silent admiration. The storyboard was finished except for accessories.

'Nice,' complimented Mandy, peeking over her shoulder. Generous praise was one of Mandy's many endearing qualities. 'But don't you think those grey and navy suits could do with a bit of sexing up?'

'Charcoal and midnight,' corrected Silky. 'And no I don't need sexing up.' The last thing Caroline Clancy wanted or needed was that.

But Mandy being Mandy was irrepressible. 'That pink is nice though. Pink to make the boys wink. Oh, and, by the way, Caroline is in the States. She'll contact us when she gets back.' That was the new Mandy. She had become casual about clients and their appointments. Not knowing or caring when Caroline would return. As for pink and winks? Silky presumed their client wouldn't be seeking anything like that.

A few mornings later, at around eleven o'clock, Mandy arrived. Her face was a Kabuki mask of despair, and the cat was clutched to her chest. Her mobile had been switched off all morning and there had been no reply from her apartment. Silky controlled herself by saying nothing. Let her PA talk herself out of this one!

But Mandy chose action rather than words. She turned the cat around carefully, so that Silky had a full view of its bandaged tail. There was silence while Silky inspected the injury. Mandy then looked at her employer again. 'I'm late, I know. But I had to go to the vet. Last night Venus bit her tail.'

The news was delivered as slowly as possible for maximum dramatic effect. Poor Mandy was transformed into a picture of abject misery. On seeing Silky, the cat mewed crankily and added a hiss. That was a cat with attitude and undeserving of the name Venus, though Mandy had sworn blind that with love and affection she'd grow into it.

'So what did the vet say?' Silky hoped she'd chosen the right question to ask. As usual, she had a desk piled high with paperwork, and telephone queries. There was a bundle of emails to be answered also. She needed Mandy to be functionally operative as soon as possible.

'He said it was self-mutilation.'

'Oh dear. How awful. Caused by what?' The query was out of Silky's mouth before she realized that it was one of those questions better left unasked.

Mandy dabbed at her eyes. 'Stress-related. Could have been brought on by feelings of isolation. Now he's put her on anti-depressants and sedatives.'

'Poor puss,' said Silky. Under these circumstances, she was relieved she hadn't confronted Mandy.

'Or it could be a compulsive disorder.'

'Oh, dear.' If she couldn't have a heart of stone, then Silky would settle for Elvis's wooden version.

'If it happens again, she'll probably have to go to a behaviour counsellor,' threatened Mandy. Tears were swapped for action. Cat and owner were obviously well suited.

'Well, you'll have to avoid stressful situations then. Perhaps she'd be better off at home.'

Mandy burst into a fresh bout of tears. This was a state of affairs that simply couldn't continue, though short of doing a Lucrezia Borgia on Cat, Silky had no notion of how to salvage the situation.

'I bought her a little travelling cage and I have it in the car,' Mandy explained hopefully.

'She was so upset, I couldn't leave her at home now, could I?'

Mandy had also perfected the when-in-doubt-ask-a-question syndrome. Heart battled with head. All Silky's instincts cried out to bring Cat into the office. There were no in-office client meetings scheduled for the day. But business was business.

Gradually Silky came to the conclusion that Cat was a lost cause – one of those situations that in business you learned to write off. She consoled herself with a pact, hinging on Cat's health. The matter came to a head however when Silky returned from a client lunch to find Mandy on her stomach on the floor of the office playing with Venus. She wasn't particularly surprised as she'd suspected Cat was in occasional residence while she was out. But suspecting was one thing, being proven right was quite another.

After weeks of recuperation and now that the bandaged tail was better, the cat's coat was rich and glossy. Judging by her cranky meows however, her first session of counselling hadn't exactly improved her disposition.

Mandy jumped immediately to her feet. With coos of affection, kisses and murmurs that, 'Mummy wouldn't be long', she lifted Cat into a decidedly luxurious travelling cage, which she then removed from Silky's desk back to her chair. She described how the counsellor had explained that sensitive cats such as Venus could feel rejected when put on the ground. She said she knew Silky would understand.

That sorted, Mandy dragged her mind back to the more mundane task of Plum business. 'Oh, and Caroline Clancy rang by the way. There's a note somewhere.' Mandy started an ineffectual search. 'Sorry, I was a bit distracted because Venus wasn't too well. I thought she was going to vomit, you know the way she . . .'

'No, I don't, Mandy,' said Silky firmly. She didn't need a description of how Venus had puked in her office, which was done in the ultimate of Georgian-rich shades of maroon. With an antique desk, complete with a tooled leather top, buttoned club chairs, and gilt-framed mirrors behind two large floral arrangements in seasonal white, her office was something of a showpiece.

Eventually, to the strains of continuous meowing from the chair, Caroline's business card was located in the overflowing paper basket. She was due to come in that very afternoon. With her photographer, Dan. On a preliminary recce. 3:30 pm to be precise. Mandy had it all noted in signature bullet points. It was now 3:25 pm.

As Silky and Mandy set about doing a frantic tidy up, the doorbell rang. Mandy opened it while Silky removed Venus from the chair to under the desk with a warning shush.

Caroline was small and dynamic, dressed in an unflattering full-skirted scarlet suit. Dan, wearing a flattering corduroy jacket with leather patches on the elbows, was lean and handsome in an artistic kind of way.

Head cocked to one side, Caroline professed delight with

the storyboard. Dan, his hands jammed into his pockets, was equally complimentary. Silky was relieved.

'I like the formality of those clothes,' said Dan, after a long pause. 'They're spot on for the kind of shoots we'll be doing. But we're looking for something to lighten Caroline's image. Any ideas?'

'How about shooting somewhere outdoors? That works well for people whose natural environment is an office.' Silky had overseen many such successful shoots and could suggest several suitable locations.

'I am not an outdoors person,' said Caroline firmly.

'Any hobbies then?' asked Dan. 'We do need some kind of an accessory.'

But Silky herself could have told him that Caroline was impossibly wedded to her career. Even her holidays were work related.

'I want something edgier than you sitting at your desk behind The Financial Times,' said Dan firmly. 'Even though the outfits are gorgeous,' he said, 'they won't be enough.'

Just then there was an irritated meow from under the desk. Silky gave an inward groan. Oh please, not now. Not when everything was going so well. Caroline and Dan cocked their ears. Mandy stooped down and lifted the cat's cage from under the desk.

'Oh, wow, what do we have here?' Dan immediately opened the door of the cage and out stepped Venus. With a flirt of her head, a raise of her tail and a deep throated purr, her white paws daintily dancing across Silky's desk.

'Hello, gorgeous,' cooed Dan.

'Where did you get her Silky? asked Caroline. 'She's beautiful.'

Mandy was in her seventh heaven. 'She's called Venus.

She's a stray. Just landed on our doorstep a few weeks ago in an awful state. Silky and I nursed her back to health.'

'Well,' said Dan, noticing Caroline's approval. 'It looks like we've found our perfect accessory.'

Marisa Mackle's books include *Mr Right for the Night*, *So Long Mr Wrong*, *Mile High Guy*, *Chinese Whispers*, *Confessions of an Air Hostess*, and *Man Hunt*.

22. PARTY ANIMAL
Marisa Mackle

The girls in No. 5 house are funny. Not as in haha but as in strange. Very strange. They never used to like me. No, in fact they used to chase me away. But then some guy they fancied said I was a cutie. Now they think I'm an addition to the place, and I get to hang around their kitchen to impress male visitors. I know, it's sad, isn't it? They even tried to get me to wear a tacky bell around my neck at one stage but I put my paw down. I have standards, you know. The girls' names are Sarah and Kate. Sarah is thin but wants to be thinner. Kate hardly eats at all which is great 'cos I get to eat all her leftovers and drink gallons of skimmed milk before it goes sour.

I used to live in number 6 with a lovely old lady who treated me like a feline princess. She rescued me when I was little but to be honest I don't remember much about my previous life as a stray. That's probably just as well because the old lady said I was thrown over a wall by a group of youths. Now you can understand why I have blocked it out of my memory. Maybe I should go for counselling. I don't like youths much. Nor do I like the yobs Sarah and Kate sometimes bring home on a Saturday night. You should see the state of them! One nearly tripped over me last weekend, coming out of Sarah's bedroom at the crack of dawn. I'm not sure what happened in the bedroom but as he was leaving in an awful hurry Sarah was shouting, 'No, I don't know any taxi numbers, ya fecking prick!'

Then, after he had left, she stumbled into the bathroom and I could hear her vomiting for ages. When I could no longer bear to listen to her retching I decided to clear off for the day. There wasn't much point sticking around anyway because Sarah and Kate are never any fun on Sundays. They always look a bit green in the face and sit around clutching their stomachs and moaning that 'there are no men out there' or that 'they're all bastards anyway'.

It's weird you know, because on Saturday evenings they're always in great form, drinking wine, getting dolled up, spraying on perfume and dancing around the sitting room to really shit disco music. I don't know why it always seems to go so horribly wrong but when I hear Kate spend about twenty minutes trying to put her key in the door, I can always tell that it's been a bad night . . . and the day after will be worse.

I wish they weren't always in such a bad mood on a Sunday because that's the only day of the week when their diets go out the window. It's the day that greasy fries are cooked and fortunately they give all the leftover fat to me.

Sarah and Kate aren't speaking this morning. They had a huge fight at about 5:00am. I know this because I was chilling in the sitting room, dreaming of mice and mayhem when the doorbell suddenly rang, blasting me out of it. Sarah had forgotten her keys and was standing with a strange man outside in the freezing cold. She kept shouting through the letterbox for Kate to open the door and I didn't know what to do. Kate had passed out on the sofa in all her clothes, with her stilettos still on her feet and her mascara streaked across her face. I did all I could to help, believe me. I tried waking Kate by pressing my nose against her cheek and then I tried licking her face. When that didn't work I ran my claws through her tights but it was no use. Every time Kate woke up she kept giving me a hug, telling me I was 'the best boy in the world' even though I'm actually female. How many times do I have to point this out?

Eventually Sarah broke a window to let herself and the man in and I took this glorious opportunity to let myself out the same window. I didn't want to be around with the two girls yelling at each other.

Sometimes I pine for the old lady. She left the house to her niece called Nina, a miserable mean-spirited yoke, who says she hates cats. How can you hate cats if you don't know any? That's like cats saying they hate humans – you can't put a whole species in one box and label it! Anyway, Nina was adamant she wanted nothing to do with me, and immediately threw my basket onto a neighbour's skip saying it stank. I refused to leave home though. I, after all, had lived there for years and she was just a newcomer.

At first I think she was afraid of me and would scream if I went near her, which was a bit odd. I mean does she think all cats go around scratching people's eyes out? What kind of rumours has she been listening to? It's only celebrity cats that throw their weight around. Or cats that have been in TV commercials. They have such big heads, you wouldn't believe it! But I'm as down to earth as they come. Give me a place to rest my head at night and a bit of milk and I'm happy.

Anyway Nina's mind was made up. She didn't like me and that was that. Not only would she not give me any decent food, but she would often insult me by throwing potato skins or mouldy bread at me. Hello? Did she think I was a walking dustbin or something? Sure you wouldn't treat a dog like that!

One night I was so unbelievably cold because Sarah and Kate were at a charity ball and Nina was sitting in as usual – she never goes out unless it's a work thing and the food and drink are free. I started scratching on the door in a pathetic attempt to attract sympathy. I know I was seriously grovelling but it had started to rain and my fur was getting soaked. Nina, of course, still refused to let me in, pretending she didn't see me crying outside the window. Eventually I took shelter under a car in a garage across the road.

However, what goes around comes around and I had something of a laugh the next morning when I hid under a bush and gleefully listened to Nina complaining to a neighbour about mice! She said that she hadn't got a wink of sleep the night before because of the scratching on the door. Luckily for me, the neighbour said the best thing to do was get a cat into the house.

Ever since I've been allowed back inside the house. Mind you, it's so boring in Nina's house. She doesn't even watch TV – she just reads books from the local library or old newspapers fished out from the neighbours' green wheelie bins. But her place is grand if I'm exhausted and just need a good kip. Heaven knows there's never a chance of forty winks over in Kate and Sarah's. When they're not screaming at each other, they're yapping into their phones or playing loud music. Sarah even stands in front of the mirror dancing with a hairbrush, but I don't think Britney needs to lose too much sleep over it!

So you see, most of the time I just have Sarah, Kate and

Nina to crash with so I have to keep them sweet. Apart
from the girls, most of the other neighbours are pretty much
non-runners. The lady doctor across the road has a nasty
yapping terrier. We've never seen eye to eye so obviously I
try and stay out of his way. And Blackie, the cat, lives in
number 4 with a big family of screaming kids. Blackie is
male and used to fancy me like hell. He was an awfully
randy so-and-so when he first moved into the area. But then
the old lady sent me for my operation as she decided she
didn't want any mini versions of me running around. I've
been ignored by Blackie ever since I came home from the
animal hospital. Men, eh? All after the one thing, that's
what I say!

Because there are so few houses on our little cul-de-sac,
there isn't much excitement. I often think of packing it all
in and heading off somewhere else. It wouldn't be too difficult as I've no luggage and no real ties to Lemon Grove
Road. But there's no way I could ever leave Mark. I love
him to bits! Sadly it's pretty much an unrequited love. Yes,
you see, although Mark often leaves me to travel overseas
with his job, I would never ever leave him to do the same.
He's the only person who looks at me as if I have feelings
of my own. He's the only person who knows that I'm not
a sly, selfish individual with no loyalty to anybody but
myself. Why do people paint all of us felines with the same
tainted brush? He calls me 'Kitty' even though I'm well into
my forties (in cat years anyway). It makes me feel young
however, and loved and wanted. And to be honest, since
the old lady died, nobody else has ever done that. Mark has
an endearing habit of stroking my head between my ears
and picking me up and cuddling me like I'm the only woman
in his life. That's kind of the way I like it. I prefer not to

have any competition. There was a woman living here for a while with Mark. She was called Clodagh and was apparently allergic to me. I would make her sneeze. At least my fur would. We didn't see eye to eye. When she came around to visit, she always insisted that Mark put me outside. And once, when Mark bought me fresh salmon for a treat and left it in the fridge, she found it and scoffed it all! When Mark came into the room he said, 'you're the best girl in the world Kitty. Wasn't that a lovely treat for you now?'

My little tummy rumbling, I kept looking at Clodagh, hoping that she'd have the decency to tell him the truth but she didn't and I went hungry that night. She'd often whine, 'Really Mark, I don't know how many times I have to ask you to put the cat out.' The cat? The cheek of her! I am so much more than just a cat.

I didn't like Clodagh at all. I just didn't think she was good enough for my Mark. Then again, I don't even think Cindy Crawford would be good enough for the man who sometimes looks at me with a glint in his eye, ruffles my fur and says, 'How about a drink then Kitty?' That's usually after he's had a particularly hard day's work in the office. During the summer we sometimes sit out in the garden. Mark will pour a bowl of ice-cold milk for me and a beer for himself. We'll sit in comfortable silence as the sun goes down behind the trees and sometimes as he closes his eyes, I will sit on his lap and purr to my heart's content. If I were human, we'd definitely be married by now. In a way, I hope Mark does meet a woman some day but for now, I'm happy with the way things are. I don't know what happened between himself and Clodagh, but he had seemed a bit down after the break up. Still things are a lot better around here now that she's gone. I want only the best for my man.

Everything's fine for the next few days until I'm around at Sarah and Kate's. Mark has gone away for a few days and I've nowhere else to hang out. Kate is complaining that I'm leaving unsightly cat fur on her cream cushions but Sarah says I'm not doing anyone any harm so Kate just decides to ignore me. Then I hear them planning their party. They're thinking of having a big barbeque. I get quite excited at the mention of the barbeque. Knowing Sarah and Kate, they'll just pretend to eat and keep throwing me their food on the grass while gulping from large glasses of wine. A barbeque? Let's bring it on!

I'm getting really excited about the party. With great interest I listen to the girls discuss the list of food they're going to buy in. Burgers (yum), sausages (yum) marshmallows (what are they?). Unfortunately though, neither of them has a huge interest in food and they swiftly move on to making up the list of eligible bachelors they want to invite. It would appear they've invited every single good-looking, successful man in the neighbourhood.

'But no dogs,' Kate makes it very clear as she scribbles down lots of names.

'Absolutely not,' Sarah agrees as she files her nails while lying across the sofa. 'And no silly bitches.'

I'm secretly glad to hear it. To be honest, it would look very odd to have a gang of canines show up to a sophisticated barbeque like this anyway.

'We have to invite some women besides ourselves though,' Kate suggests almost as an afterthought.

'Well maybe one or two then . . . ,' Sarah reluctantly agrees. 'How about that one across the road? I can never remember her name?'

'Kate raises an eyebrow. 'You mean Nina? The civil

servant? No bloody way. She came round here borrowing milk the other day and never replaced it. Every time she calls in she has one arm longer than the other. We're not having her. Jesus, we want this to be a glamorous affair, not some dowdy knees-up with the neighbours.'

Gosh, they're being quite catty (pardon the pun) today. I think I'll head off for a stroll and leave them at it. However I'm just about to skip out the window when I hear them mention the name 'Mark'. I stand frozen to the spot. Now this I have to hear.

'Isn't he the one who helped you start your car last week?' asks Kate. 'Oh yes, invite him by all means.

'He's pretty cute,' says Sarah. 'But he's mine, do you hear? I saw him first!'

You can hiss off, I think indignantly, Mark is *mine*! I storm off angrily. Neither of those girls would suit Mark. All they do is drink and fight about men. Neither of them would be able to put a decent meal in front of him or snuggle up to him tenderly the way I do. Mind you, they're both good-looking girls and men can be very foolish in the company of such girls. I've seen both Kate and Sarah reduce grown men to tears. I can't afford to let Mark fly into their web. Over the next few days I monitor the situation carefully. Kate writes out the invitations and puts them in big pink envelopes but doesn't post them for ages. If I could read, I think I'd just remove Mark's invite but I can't.

Eventually Kate posts all the envelopes. Now I just have to wait for Mark to get back from his latest business trip to Moscow. Two days later I see him parking his BMW at the gate and I run over to say hello. He scoops me up in his arms and plants a big kiss between my ears. 'It's good to see you Kitty. I've got a little surprise for you too.' Then

he puts me back down on the ground and I rush between
his legs as he puts the key in the door. I desperately need
to get this invitation. However there's so much mail on the
floor. I can't see it. It must be buried somewhere underneath
the pile.

Painstakingly slowly Mark opens his post groaning at the
amount of bills. Suddenly I see the pink envelope peeking
out from behind an automobile magazine. I'm filled with
panic. Suppose Mark opens it and reads it and falls in love
with Sarah or Kate? Where would that leave me? Oh dear
sometimes a girl's just got to do what a girl's got to do. I
squat down on top of the magazine and invitation and when
Mark notices the trickle his eyes widen in horror.

'Kitty! What on earth are you doing?' He picks me up
in the middle of 'doing my business' by the scruff of my
neck and throws me outside. The indignity and humiliation
is terrible but hopefully it will be worth it in the end, I think
wincing.

'You're disgusting,' Mark scolds as I hang my head in
shame. 'I had brought home a tin of caviar for you but I
don't think I'll give it to you now.'

Caviar? I don't believe it!

'I'll have to throw this stuff out now,' he says huffily,
donning a pair of rubber gloves and scooping up the magazine, along with the pink envelope holding the dreaded
invitation. He brings them out to the garden and sticks them
in the bin. I give a huge sigh of relief. Mission accomplished.

Mark ignores me for about a day but because I'm so cute
eventually he gives in and can't help patting my head. I
preen with pride in front of him and eventually he gives up
ignoring me. We're friends again.

Sunday is a beautiful sunny day and the girls are preparing

their barbeque. They tell me to shove off when they see me hanging around the food so I make myself scarce. I'm in no mood for a catfight today. Mark is in the garden sunning himself. He's got a body that would make women go weak at the knees for, but I'm just a cat so my knees are fine. I climb onto his torso and go to sleep.

I'm woken up by the sound of Nina's voice. What the hell does she want? She can sod off with herself if she thinks I'll help her get together with Mark. I just ignore her but she has the cheek to hang around the gate like a stale fart. I wish she would stop peering in at us. Now, I know I may be a little bit biased but Mark is an incredible looking guy. He's tall dark, and handsome, and what's more, he has a great job, drives a sports car, has lots of money and is very kind. Nina, on the other hand, is not at all generous, isn't glamorous, never wears make up or gets her hair done, and only goes out for a night if someone else is paying. She is definitely not a good match for Mark. I didn't get rid of the other two hussies to leave Mark free for Nina!

Anyway she's still bloody there, standing at the gate in a white t-shirt with a beer logo that she'd got free in a pub one night and a pair of old jeans. And although, I hate to admit it, she doesn't look half bad at all. Her arms are tanned as the result of lying in the sun for the last few days, and her long dark hair is swept off her face into a high ponytail.

'Hello,' she calls over the wall, in a big friendly voice.

Mark looks up and says hello back in a warm welcoming tone of voice. I continue to ignore her.

'I'm just looking for my cat.'

'Oh, is this your cat?' he sounds surprised. 'I've always wondered who she belonged to. She's gorgeous, isn't she?

I'm mad about her. Cats are just the best, aren't they?'

'Er, yes. Well come on Snuggles, pish wish wish wish . . .'

Snuggles? How dare she! As if I would answer to a name like that! I stand up, arch my back and stare coldly at her. She comes towards me, giggling for Mark's benefit obviously. What an irritating girl!

I wait until she comes right up to me, and as soon as she reaches me, I turn and I run like hell through Mark's front door, up the stairs and into his bedroom. I hop onto the windowsill and spit down at Nina who is obviously livid she couldn't follow me into the house. As I sit on the sill trying to get my breath back, I hear Mark ask Nina if I'm really her cat.

'Of course,' Nina says, flushing a deep shade of red.

'It's just that normally Kitty is so friendly to everyone. She doesn't seem to know you.'

'Kitty?'

'That's what I call her. She likes the name. I must say I find her fabulous company. She could almost be human!'

Oh God, don't insult me.

Nina looks at me open-mouthed like an idiot.

I glare back.

'Oh, well . . . I'd best be off then,' said Nina hurriedly.

'Good-bye. I never got your name?'

'Nina.'

'Good-bye Nina.'

'Yes good-bye,' I mutter under my breath. 'And good riddance! Now, where's that tin of caviar?'

Roxanne Parker is a freelance journalist. Her work includes publication in *Image, Irish Independent, Irish Tatler, Sunday World* and *Evening Herald*.

23. AN UNEXPECTED VISITOR
Roxanne Parker

The key turned with a satisfying click as the door opened smoothly. David was greeted by the flawless empty expanse of oak floor, which made up his hall. Spacious white walls and a clutter-free interior ensured that the ying was well and truly balanced with the yang. He let out a gentle sigh as yet another day in the office had come to an end. Looking at his home, David was filled with an over-whelming sense that all was well with the world. He felt the weight of the day's worries dissolve in a pool at his feet as he stepped over the threshold and into his peaceful sanctuary. Placing his briefcase in the hidden panelled press concealed behind the door, he headed straight for the garden. The last of the sun gathered itself in the borders of his simple patio complete with minimalist, Japanese-inspired water formation, which was guarded by a moss-covered Budda statue. Yes it was a perfect sun spot, David thought contently.

His eyes fell fondly on the neat rows of rocket and basil he had planted at the back of the garden. He admired the leafy ferns and the oriental grasses, which grazed the pool-side. 'A place for every thing and everything in its place', David smiled to himself as he pulled out a cream canvas teak deckchair and turned his face to the last rays of the wavering evening sun.

The garden was so peaceful; it had been worth all the hours labouring to turn this humble squat on the banks of the river Liffey into his own retreat. As an architect David had gritted his teeth for years dealing with narrow-minded county council members who had no concept of design, not to mention the countless private clients he had to entertain who had more money than taste. Time and time again David would have to bite back his tongue as yet another lady-who-lunched type pulled out a copy of Elle Décor pointing at a shot of a living room coated with gold flock wallpaper. The woman's eyes would shine with hope and desperation in a bid to outdo the neighbours in the style stakes.

'Why not?' she'd whinge as David tried to calmly explain that what might be considered 'ironic cool' this season would just be thought of as pure naff the next. He visibly grimaced when he recalled penny-pinching local council members trying to implement cost cutting procedures over one of his timeless designs. But he was quickly soothed by the thought that at last he had a house to call his own, with which he was allowed to do exactly whatever he liked. The pleasure he derived from choosing the darkest slate tiles for the kitchen, and an original Georgian table for his open plan living room mixed with vintage 1950s lamps sourced and shipped from a specialist store on the Lower East Side in New York, was immense. Every time he felt frustrated in work or faced yet another client with a serious case of taste deficiency, he would simply think of his little home and would immediately feel calmer. It was his secret weapon against the world, a retreat where he could transport his mind and escape in his daydreams.

He had saved hard to buy his little home. Chapelizod was not a hip neighbourhood when he bought his dilapidated property. The place had to be completely gutted and shelled. It had taken the best part of two years to complete and it had stretched David's finances to the limit. But he had had the vision to see the property's worth. Nestled between the Phoenix Park's protected land and the banks of the river Liffey, Chapelizod was one of the few areas left in Dublin that had no room for major development, yet was only minutes from the city centre and his office. In the three years since he had moved, his house had trebled in value and one property owner had sold out to a developer who was now building apartments at the back of David's garden. A slight setback but nothing too drastic.

The only blemish David could recall on his beautiful home was the time his French girlfriend had tried to redecorate. He remembered with a shudder returning home from work to find Anouk standing proudly, paintbrush in hand, next to a freshly painted moss-green wall.

'Don't you just love it?' she purred in her heavy Parisian accent. David could feel his jaw drop. He surveyed the destruction of his beautiful home. A hideous suede couch complete with matching choca-mocha-latte throw cushions festooned the floor. Cube footstools and sheepskin throws drowned out his beautiful pure oak floor, which had cost him over fifteen grand to install. His home, his sacred clutter-free abode looked like a bloody style bar off Grafton Street! It was horrific – far too much to take in. David could feel the colour drain from his face, feel the blood rising to his head in a dizzy wave of heat. Without being able to form the words properly in his mouth, he croaked, 'what have you done?'

Before an astonished Anouk could respond, David found the words he was looking for, 'Out! Get out now!'

'But don't you like it darling?' Anouk retorted slightly lowering the paintbrush she held clenched in her fist. David almost felt that the moss paint staining the bristles was his very own blood and guts, and that Anouk had punctured his soul by destroying the one thing that was most sacred to him.

'But I just wanted to make the place look nice, make it look more homely. It needed a woman's touch,' pouted Anouk. 'It was just so plain, so bare . . . ,' her voice trailed off as she caught David's eye. It was obvious by looking at him that she had over stepped the mark.

The following evening, the footstools, rugs and throw cushions where all sent back to Habitat, and Anouk went back to France. The next weekend David headed straight to Atlantic Homecare and bought four litres of white paint.

'That's the problem with the French – they think they have better taste than everyone else on the planet,' David mumbled to himself as he purified his walls. He had been told how to do up other people's homes for too long, and there was no way he was now going to be told to do up his own house.

As the sun cooled in the sky, Dave felt the tension evaporate from his body with the wavering daylight. He felt totally relaxed until he heard a rustle from the Pampas grass at the edge of the garden. His eyes flickered open momentarily only to be greeted by the sight of a fluffy white kitten emerging from the shrubbery, closely followed by a larger black and white version, which was obviously the mother. The pair sat unblinking, staring back at David. Stunned at their nonchalance, he was momentarily mesmerised by the intensity of their gaze. For one fleeting moment he thought how cute the pair looked as the mother tenderly licked the kitten's ear. But then outrage at the arrogance of these trespassers swept through David and before he knew it he was on his feet, reaching for the yard broom and charging down the garden with all his limbs failing dementedly as he whooped and roared.

He was determined to defend his pond crammed with over three hundred euro worth of Japanese carp, which peacefully swam through the still waters. Determined to defend his plants, which he had handpicked from garden centres throughout Ireland and which he laboured over every weekend after labouring all week in the office. Determined to defend his property from these unwelcome and uninvited hooligans who would chase all the birds from the garden and bury their toxic waste in his soil poisoning his shrubs. The cats leapt to attention, sprinting across the lawn and hurled themselves behind the shelter of the garden shed. Like a man possessed, David poked the broom handle under the shed jabbing and prodding in an attempt to rid the cats from his property. Like a swirl of grey smoke, the mother cat sprang from her hiding place and scaled the garden wall in one exaggerated leap, escaping to the neighbour's garden. The kitten straining to keep up, took one look at the wall before turning and darting in the opposite direction. Sucking in its furry belly the kitten squeezed through a gap in the fence.

'And don't come back!' David roared at the garden wall shaking the broom in his fist. Determinedly he went into the shed and reappeared moments later clutching a sheet of chicken wire, which he rammed unmercifully between the gap in the fence and the wall, ensuring the offenders could never return.

The next day at work, as David sat doggedly going through plans for a new library in Cork, his thoughts drifted to the furry white kitten. He felt a momentary pang of remorse as he recalled the frightened ball of fur hurtling through the neighbour's fence. Had it found its mother? Was it still alone?

'So have you come up with a solution for wheelchair access to the library yet?'

David's mind sprang back to the present as Shona, one of the other architects working on the Cork-based project, approached.

'I think I've got it covered Shona.'

'Good, I was just seeing if you needed a hand'

'It's under control, now if you'll excuse me I'm running late for my meeting in Cork with the site manager.'

David scooped up the plans he had been studying into his briefcase, while heading for the door without so much as a backwards glance.

Shona's such a leftie, David thought to himself. Trust her to interfere with his project asking about wheelchair access when the structure of the building hadn't even been designed. She was such a hippy. Those wild unkempt curls, her sloppy layered, long dresses worn with cardigans permanently coated in cat hair. Shona volunteered two evenings a week in the local animal shelter. She was a textbook example of a tree-hugger.

She had once tried to bond with David when she joined the office two months ago and saw that he cycled into work.

'You're a cyclist too,' she beamed with her ridiculously wholesome complexion shining with enthusiasm.

'I take the bike in every day, rain or shine,' she added proudly.

The woman lived in Howth and their offices were in Donnybrook. She was clearly a nutcase. David on the other hand cycled into work as it took a mere thirty minutes on the bike and it meant he avoided wasting time sitting in rush-hour traffic. His motivation for cycling was to save himself time, not the environment. Of course he had a car as well – how on earth was he supposed to visit the sites he was working on all over the country without one?

I'd like to see Shona cycle to Cork to work on the project then! David laughed to himself.

That evening David didn't make it home until after nine. His eyes burned with tiredness from the long drive, and his head throbbed with the problems he faced on his latest building. Heading for the kitchen he filled up the kettle and took a carton of milk from the fridge neatly pouring himself a glass. He couldn't abide people who took a slug from the carton – it was such a filthy habit. He leaned his tired head against the cool glass door, which opened onto the garden. Movement caught his eye and a white beam of moonlight glimmered against the pond. David choked on his milk. There, paw precisely placed in mid air, stroking the water's edge and clawing at the golden shimmer of his precious carp was the contraband white kitten.

'Get away,' he hissed thumping the glass. 'Shoo, go on, get out of here.'

The kitten raised its pink nose from the water's edge and gazed inquisitively at the source of such outrage. David flung the door open in preparation to run the kitten from his turf, but still the kitten stood his ground. David roared, the kitten purred. As David approachd, the kitten wound itself around David's ankles, purring, pushing and preening its face against the fabric of his trousers. David was gobsmacked at the audacity of this creature. Single handedly it had gate-crashed his garden and was now trying to worm his way into his house. Well, David was having none of it.

He bent down to disentangle the furry mess from his legs, but the kitten nuzzled his palm with his silky fur. He is awfully cute, David thought to himself.

'Where's your mother?' he questioned, thawing as he stroked the kitten's soft fur. He looked around the garden but the mother cat was nowhere to be found. The kitten was alone. David thought guiltily of his behaviour in the garden the previous day. He must have scared the mother away and now she had abandoned her kitten. The kitten was alone and it was David's fault. Patting its fluffy head, David went into the kitchen and retrieved the milk and poured the kitten a small bowl. The kitten eagerly lapped it up.

'Now that should keep you going and keep you out of my pond. But you can't stay, this is just for tonight.'

As David watched the kitten lick the bowl clean he felt a wave of affection for the animal, but there really was no way he could give the kitten a home, he just wasn't a cat person.

Autumn rolled in and with it the rusty hues of the changing seasons. The white kitten became a regular visitor to David's garden and every day he left food out for it. 'This is just so you stay away from the birds and don't invade my garden pond,' David would say as he laid out the food and stroked the cat's back. Its limbs had stretched into adolescence, but its blue unblinking eyes remained unchanged. David had taken to calling him Kimberley, after the Jacob's marsh-mallow biscuits. Sometimes the cat rolled on the patio exposing his fluffy belly for David to scratch. 'Well you're definitely a tom-cat that's for sure,' thought David ruefully as he rubbed the cat's soft under-belly. Although he never admitted it to himself, he began to look forward to Kimberly's visits. But David remained adamant the cat was merely a visitor and not his pet.

David's project in Cork was making progress. There were some problems but every time he made his weekly pilgrimage to the site with Shona in tow, babbling about the benefits of recycling in the passenger seat, things seemed to have advanced nicely. David was beginning to warm to Shona's company. She may have been slightly batty but her constant flow of friendly chat and her idealism was a refreshing break from the city sarcasm David faced every day from his urban friends.

'You're so uptight,' Shona teased as they drove back from Cork one evening.

'Well if I'm uptight, then you're a flake. What's that on your jumper? Cat hair! Don't tell me you're one of those women who lives alone with a gaggle of cats in your house.'

'I've only two and they're lovely. They're much better company than some people I could mention,' she said scowling in David's direction.

'Disease-ridden, flea-bitten moggies, that's all they are,' David retorted

'If you spent a day in the animal shelter you wouldn't say that. They're innocent creatures. It's their owners who should be put in cages not the animals. The way some of them treat their pets, they should be locked up.'

'Don't be daft Shona, they're vermin, disease-carriers. They should be put down, the lot of them before they can breed anymore and infest the countryside.'

'You can be such a heartless bastard sometimes David – do you know that? I wouldn't swap an hour's time with my cats for a thousand acres of your white property-obsessed minimalist life. There's more to life than building and material things. A house can't love you David but at least an animal can. For somebody who designs buildings for living people you sure seem to hate surrounding yourself with life.'

'Just because I don't like cats, now I'm a miserable bastard? You have got to be kidding me!'

'It's nothing to do with the cats. It's everything David. It's the way you look down on Siobhan the receptionist because she drinks in Temple Bar at the weekends. It's the way you sneer at Tom in work for shopping in Aldi while you go to Marks and Spencer's. It's the way you act so superior to everyone.'

The pair sat in icy silence for the rest of the journey. Things in the office were little improved as Shona made a point of ignoring David. He pretended to brush it off but secretly he felt hurt by Shona's tirade. Was there any truth in what she had said?

Winter hung in the air like a dreaded appointment. The air cooled and the light faded but Kimberly still made his daily pilgrimage to David's garden. By now his fur had sprouted into a wispy, glossy long coat and his body had stretched to its full size. As frost grazed the earth with its frozen touch, David began to bring Kimberly inside.

'It's just for tonight,' David would mumble by way of explanation. 'There's frost on the ground tonight.'

Without paying the slightest bit of attention, Kimberly trotted inside and headed straight for the fire. David eyed him suspiciously. For a feral cat he seemed exceptionally accustomed to his creature comforts as he lay resplendent on the rug.

One night turned into the whole winter as evening after evening, Kimberly scurried under David's legs and bolted for his place by the fire. It was strange but the house felt more homely with this bundle of fur by the fire.

'Artists are supposed to have a muse,' David contemplated. 'Some of the most renowned artists in the world had a cat as a pet to help inspire them'.

David had to admit he liked having Kimberly around, he found it comforting. Not so comforting was the frosty divide between himself and Shona. The drives down to Cork which had once been a bit of fun were now a dreaded strain as both of them sat wordlessly throughout the journeys.

Did you hear that Shona's moved to Chapelizod?' said Siobhan, the receptionist, one lunch-time, through a mouthful of Taytos.

'When?' David replied, slightly alarmed.

'Last week.' Siobhan's eyes were gleaming as she sensed David's discomfort. 'She moved into one of the new apartments built on the banks of the Liffey. Isn't that near where you live?'

David felt nauseous. Those were the newly built apartments that over looked his little garden. They were right next-door to his home!

'She wanted to be nearer the office now that she knows her job is permanent. I reckon the cycle from Howth every day was killing her.'

'Great!' fumed David under his breath. 'Now not only would he have to spend his time in the office avoiding Shona but he would have to watch his back in Chapelizod too. There was only one local shop and two pubs in the village. There would be no escaping her.

That evening David made a point of leaving the office long after Shona. He had a nightmare image of the two of them unlocking their bikes simultaneously, passing each other out

spitefully on their bikes as they drag-raced each other down
the quays the whole journey back to Chapelizod. There was
no way he was spoiling his nice cycle home by being confronted
with that fuzzy-haired animal lover on her banger of a bike.

Looking left and right David checked the lay of the land
before entering the village shop after work. No sign of Shona.
Good. She was probably hanging out in the animal shelter
with her flea-friends.

He stocked up on several tins of cat food. Rummaging
in his briefcase for his wallet, he waited for the elderly man
in front of him to pay for his cigarettes. Before he could
make a clean escape, he felt a presence enter the shop. Shona
looked curiously at David while he frantically tried to conceal
his cans of cat food.

'Hello David, dining alone again I see?' she smirked before
heading to the back of the shop.

Back in the safety of his house David fumbled in a kitchen
drawer for a tin opener. He opened the back door to let
Kimberly in but there was no sign of him. David called
again. He looked around the garden but the snowy cat was
nowhere to be seen. It was the first time in seven months
that Kimberly hadn't appeared. David gnawed his lip in
concern. He hoped he was okay.

The night aged and David fell asleep alone in front of
the TV with a congealed bowl of penne with pesto and sun-
dried tomatoes half eaten at his feet. Outside a weak noise
made itself known, rising in tempo by the minute. David
awoke, freeing his eyes from the cement-like grit of sleep
and groaned uncomfortably. He had a crick in his neck from
falling asleep on the couch.

'Meow' the noise increased in urgency. David swerved his
head to the source.

'Kimberly!' he exclaimed. The cat had his nose pressed against the window glaring in at David. He opened the door and the cat sprinted through David's legs to warm itself by the dwindling embers of the fire.

'Where have you been? Eh?' He smoothed the animal's fur.

Kimberly nuzzled his hand, ignoring the bowl of food David laid out for him. Instead he trotted off to his basket and promptly fell asleep

Throughout December Kimberly continued his disappearing acts. Sometimes he ate but mostly he slept ignoring David. Christmas came and went and so did Kimberly. When he returned he looked fat and he wore a blue velvet collar around his neck with a silver bell.

Davie removed it in a temper. Who on earth was trying to steal his cat?

That day he picked up a silver collar in town and secured it round the cat's neck. That will teach that cat thief not to mess with his cat, he thought smugly, flinging the blue velvet collar in the bin.

The following day, David invited a couple of friends over to his house for New Year's Eve. They arranged to meet in the local pub first, but the night looked like it was about to be soured by the presence of Shona who was sitting primly at the bar. Relations had become increasingly strained between them. Shona had taken to getting the train down to Cork when she needed to visit the site. She would cycle to Heuston Station and chain her bike to the railings outside. The station was a mere ten minute cycle from her home. David had stopped shopping in the village store to avoid Shona. Instead he bought a pair of pannier bags for his bike and he loaded them with groceries from Donnybrook.

But now here she was, a woman on a mission with a pint of Guinness in one hand and an expression of hardened determination as she marched across the pub. As her golden hair bounced around her shoulders, David had to admit she looked very pretty. She wore a dusky pink dress, which hugged her lean figure, and across her shoulders she had carelessly draped a lilac shawl.

'Who's she?' asked Sean, one of David's friends, his voice full of undisguised admiration.

'Oh just some girl from work.'

'She's hot,' Sean replied enthusiastically without tearing his eyes away from the approaching figure.

'She's a pain in the ass.'

'Well, if you're not interested do you mind if I make a move?'

'Be my guest.'

Shona was now standing in front of the group. 'Happy New Year, well, almost,' she beamed before plonking the pint in front of David.

'Oh, Happy New Year, it's eh, good to see you,' stuttered David as his friends rolled their eyes and nudged him waiting for their personal introduction to this babe.

David took his cue.

'Shona I'd like you to meet some friends of mine. This is Paddy, Sean and Brian.'

'Lovely to meet you,' Shona said smiling widely.

The lads sat up straight competing with one another to see who could give the most charming introduction. Sean went over the top kissing the back of Shona's hand. She dissolved in a fit of giggles.

'David, come on over and meet my friends,' Shona demanded, pulling David to his feet.

When they were out of earshot from his friends, Shona whispered, 'look David, this thing has gone on much too long. It's New Year's Eve so let's bury the hatchet.'

'Where would you like me to bury it?' David retorted.

'I'm serious. We're both adults so it's time we start acting that way.'

David grudgingly shook hands and bought Shona a pint of organic cider. As the night progressed David asked Shona and her friends if they'd like to come over to his house with the rest of the gang. Needless to say the lads were all delighted with the female additions to the party.

Shona was surprisingly upbeat. She played *Scissor Sisters* loudly on the stereo, which, of course David strongly protested to. But there was nothing he could do to stop her. She danced around the living room, spinning and spiralling around David's friends.

'She's a cool girl,' Sean whispered to David.

Taking a long drag on his cigarette David swung his head as the back door opened and Shona emerged.

'There you are!' she exclaimed. 'Come on inside, it's almost midnight.'

'I just want to finish my smoke,' David said indicating to the half-lit cigarette in his hand.

'I didn't know you smoked.'

'I don't.'

'Can I have one?'

'I didn't know you smoked,' exclaimed David.

'I don't,' Shona replied with a sparkle in her eye. 'But sometimes it's nice not to be so perfect.'

The pair sat in comfortable silence for a moment, lost in their thoughts and their cigarettes.

David stole a look at her from the corner of his eye. She

really looked so beautiful sitting there with the moonlight reflecting on her golden hair.

A soft tinkling noise disturbed David's thought as Kimberley emerged from the bushes returned from his wanderings. His white coat was knotted with twigs and he looked plumper and was sporting yet another blue velvet collar and bell.

'Kimberly, there you are!' Where have you been boy? Eh?' The cat purred loudly and pushed his body against David's legs.

Shona looked on totally dumbstruck.

'Who's put that awful bell around your neck again? Eh?' asked David as he nuzzled the cat.

'What are you doing with my cat?' started Shona.

'*Your* cat?' What are you talking about? This is *my* cat. This is Kimberly. I've had him since he was a kitten.'

'Nonsense, David. That's Snowflake. He's a stray and I adopted him when I found him howling outside my apartment door. The poor thing was obviously starving.'

'Does he look like a stray? I spend a fortune on cat food, trust me he's well looked after.'

'But everybody knows you hate cats! You said it yourself. Flea-ridden pests, that's what you called them.'

'I know but I just sort of adopted this fella,' explained David as the cat curled round his ankles. I'm also the one who put the silver collar on him. Did it not raise your suspicions that he might not be a stray? Look Shona, I've a cat basket inside and everything. This fella is very much my pet.'

Shona thought back to the time she met David in the local shop laden with cat food. She also remembered Snowflake returning with a sparkly silver collar around his neck, but she had just thought that kids had put it on him for Christmas.

It was hard to believe that someone as selfish as David would ever have time for anyone but himself – let alone a cat!

With that Kimberly slid passed David, tail dismissively in the air and nested with a friendly meow next to Shona.

Inside they could hear the count down for the New Year. 'Ten, nine, eight . . .'

Shona looked at David in amazement. She had always thought of him as a cold, unfeeling creature yet here he was tenderly stoking the cat. Her cat! Their cat?'

'I suppose I'll have to apply for visitation rights,' she smiled.

The cat jumped on her knee and lazily rested his paws on David's lap. He looked at Kimberley curled up between them, before looking back at Shona.

'First you land in on my office, then in my village and now you're even trying to take my cat!'

'Maybe someone's trying to tell us something,' Shona said softly.

The cat yawned lazily.

'Six, five, four, three, two . . .'

Before David knew what he was doing he leaned across and kissed Shona. 'Happy New Year!'

Party poppers and a chorus of Auld Lang Syne exploded from inside. In the distance, a riot of colour illuminated the night's sky as fireworks spun through the darkness.

But as the pair sat entwined, neither of them heard a thing except for the gentle purr of Kimberly who lay sandwiched between them, and the beating of their hearts, which drowned out all other noise.

Colette Caddle's books include
*Red Letter Day, A Cut Above, Forever FM,
It's All About Him, Shaken and Stirred,
Changing Places* and
The Betrayal of Grace Mulcahy.

www.colettecaddle.com

24. MUMMY WOULDN'T BUY ME A BOW WOW

Colette Caddle

Katie loved dogs. She wanted one of her very own. She pleaded with her mother on almost a daily basis, but Trish bought her daughter a goldfish instead. Katie wasn't impressed and Fishy only survived five weeks. The pet shop owner said that fish usually died because of overfeeding, but Trish suspected it had more to do with her son, Sam who hugged it at every opportunity. Unfortunately Fishy wasn't always quick enough to avoid the three-year-old's eager little fingers.

Then Trish bought Katie a hamster. The pet shop owner told her that hamsters were very successful pets for young children – low maintenance but fun and cuddly. Katie was marginally more interest in Hammy the hamster, but it didn't last.

'Hamster's are boring,' she announced after a few days. 'I want a dog.'

'I'm not going to give in,' Trish assured her friend, Viv, on the phone. 'How would I ever cope? Dogs need to be walked, washed and they poo and wee everywhere.'

'And the big ones cost a fortune to feed. Not like my little Troy.' Viv smiled down at her beloved Terrier.

'You can just bet that Katie would pick the biggest. No, there's no way it's going to happen. Muggins here would end up looking after it and I have enough on my plate.' Trish looked across at Sam who was carefully lining up soggy cornflakes along the edge of the table, while baby Georgie squirmed on her lap as he tried to make a grab for her mug.

'I'd better go, Viv. The monsters are getting out of control.'

'Okay Babes, I'll call you in a couple of days. And when the going gets tough just remember, in less than three weeks' time, you'll be relaxing in the health spa and your biggest problem will be deciding what to have for dinner.'

'Oh, bliss!' Trish said goodbye to her friend and hung up. She was really looking forward to the overnight break at the health spa in Wicklow. It was something she never ever thought she'd be able to afford, but her mother had given her five hundred euro for her thirtieth birthday with the directive that she must spend it all on herself. Trish knew immediately what she wanted to do and Declan had happily volunteered to take the two days off to look after the children.

'Are you sure you don't mind?' she'd asked him.

'Of course not, honey, you could do with a break from this lot and we should just about manage to get through forty-eight hours without killing each other.'

Trish knew her husband was in for a shock. Looking after the three Ryan children was a full-time job. Still, he'd cope. She released the wriggling Georgie on to the floor to play, and sipped her tea while she daydreamed about the health spa. It would be so nice to have no responsibilities for a change. No nappies to change, no clothes to wash, no floors to clean – she winced as she spied the mushy spread of cornflakes and toast crumbs under Sam's chair. The thought of sleeping uninterrupted in a comfy bed and getting breakfast served up to her the next morning was enough to make her go weak at the knees.

It was late on Friday afternoon, there were only ten days to go to her little holiday and yes, Trish was counting them. She hummed quietly to herself as she put sausages under the grill. She loved Friday evenings. She always fed the kids early and then when they were in bed, she and Declan would open a bottle of wine, order Chinese food and watch a good film. Sometimes, they even had a little cuddle on the sofa.

'Mama, doggy,' Sam called excitedly from his position by the window.

'Yes, darling,' Trish said, as she checked to see if the potatoes were soft yet.

'Doggy, doggy,' Sam repeated.

'Bow-wow,' confirmed Georgie from his bouncy chair.

'Mammy?' Katie pulled open the patio door.

'Yes, Katie?' Trish looked up and smiled at her daughter's flushed, excited face.

'Come and look.'

'Not now, darling, I'm getting dinner.'

'Mammy, please, Mammy,' Katie whined.

Trish crossed the room to see what all the fuss was about. 'What is it? Oh no!'

Her eyes dropped to the skinny, bedraggled little dog, at Katie's feet. 'What on earth are you doing with that scruffy thing? Where did you get him? Who does he belong to?'

'I don't know. He just appeared out of nowhere.' Katie looked down at the dog with adoring eyes.

'Well he can disappear back to nowhere. Come in and

wash your hands, it's nearly dinner time.' Trish dragged her daughter inside. 'Shoo,' she said to the dog who promptly sat down and wagged its tail at her.

She closed the door on him and turned away. 'Go and wash your hands, Katie,' she repeated. 'You too, Sam.'

'Wanna play with doggy.' Sam told her.

'Bow-wow,' Georgie clapped his hands in delight.

'I don't need this,' Trish muttered under her breath, wondering how she could distract the children long enough to give the mongrel a helping toe out of her garden. 'Sausages for dinner,' she said brightly to Sam who loved his food.

'Wanna play with doggy,' he said, his mouth settling into a stubborn line.

'You can't,' Trish snapped, 'he's a naughty doggy who'd bite you.'

'He would not!' Her daughter returned from the bathroom in time to hear this slanderous remark. 'He's gentle and loving, he's the perfect dog.'

'He's skinny, he's ugly, and he's probably got fleas,' Trish retorted and went to strain the potatoes. 'Now, who wants beans?'

'I'm not hungry,' Katie said, crouching down by the door and gazing out at the dog.

'Not hungry,' echoed Sam, 'wanna play with doggy.'

Trish mashed the potatoes with a vengeance. 'We don't know anything about that doggy, he might be dangerous. Besides,' she said quickly before Katie could interrupt, 'his owner will be worried about him.'

'Hey, where is everybody?'

Trish heaved a sigh of relief as her husband appeared in the doorway and his two eldest children ran to hug him. 'Good timing dear.'

'Oh?' Declan met his wife's eyes over their heads.

'We've got a doggy!' Katie exclaimed.

'Doggy, doggy!' Sam jumped up and down and then ran to the window to point at his new very best friend.

'Bow-wow!' Georgie gave his father a gummy grin.

'He's not your doggy,' Trish said through gritted teeth.

'But he wants to be,' Katie protested. 'He followed me everywhere all afternoon, Daddy. He wants to be with me, just me,' she added giving Sam a superior look.

'I see.'

'I've explained to Katie that the dog must go back to its owner,' Trish said with a meaningful look at her husband.

'Yes, Katie, Mammy's right.'

'Now sit up at the table please.'

Trish served up dinner, settled Georgie in his high chair and spooned mashed vegetables into his mouth. 'Someone is probably out looking for him right now.'

Declan looked from his wife to the little dog who didn't look as if he'd had a meal or a wash in quite some time. 'You think?'

Trish glared at him. 'Eat up Sam, your dinner is getting cold.'

Her son reluctantly picked up a sausage. Trish was about to tell him to use his fork, but at least he was eating which was more than could be said for his sister. Katie was sitting looking from her plate to the little dog, whose nose was pressed against the glass, tongue hanging out.

'Come on, Katie, eat something,' Declan said gently.

'I can't eat with him looking at me.'

Trish sighed. 'Declan would you give the dog some potato and a drink of water, please?'

'Oh, Mammy, thank you!'

Katie's eyes lit up and Trish couldn't help smiling. 'Well, I suppose a little food won't hurt but then Daddy's going to put him outside.'

Katie's face fell. 'But it will be dark soon and he'll be frightened.'

'Nonsense, dogs aren't afraid of the dark. He'll be fine. Now eat your dinner please.'

Katie obediently picked up her fork but only nibbled her food.

'Look, Mammy,' Sam giggled pointing out the window, 'Doggy walks funny.'

Trish watched as the dog ran around the garden. He was hopping, not putting his rear left paw to the ground at all. The poor little thing must have been in an accident.

'I'm going to call him Hopper,' Katie announced.

'Probably very apt,' Declan murmured.

Trish sighed. 'You're not calling him anything because he's not yours. He already has a name.'

Katie made a face. 'Well, we can't keep calling him Doggy.'

'You won't have to call him anything because it's nearly bedtime and he won't be here when you wake up.'

'But he was,' Trish wailed to Viv when she called for a chat a few days later. 'It looked as if he hadn't moved all night, and when I opened the door he almost turned himself inside out with excitement. Declan said we'd have to take him in, at least until we found the owner.'

'Katie must have been over the moon,' Viv laughed.

'Oh, in seventh heaven. Anyway, we put notices up all over the place yesterday but we haven't had one phone call. Still, I can't say I'm surprised, the dog looks neglected. The owner probably hasn't even noticed he's gone.'

'The bastard should be put up against a wall and shot,'

Viv railed, bending to kiss the tip of her own pet's nose. 'Why do people buy dogs if they're not going to look after them?'

'I don't know, Viv. Hopper may be a bit bedraggled but I must admit he's a very affectionate, funny little thing.'

'So what are you going to do if you can't find the owner?' Viv asked.

'I don't suppose you'd like to take him in?'

'I'd love to, Trish, but my garden is barely big enough for one dog never mind two.'

'Oh, well, it was just an idea.'

'Will you keep him?'

'I really don't want to, Viv. It would be different if Sam and Georgie were a bit older, but right now taking in a dog just adds to my work load.'

'Oh, don't worry, Trish, it's early days. You'll probably get a call tonight.'

But there were no calls that night or the next and it was time to decide what to do.

'Couldn't we just take him to the dog pound?' Trish suggested, still overwhelmed at the idea of another "baby" to look after.

'We could but you know what will happen to him there.'

'You think they'd put him down?'

'Well, I can't see people queuing up to adopt a skinny, lame mutt like him, can you?'

Trish sighed. 'I suppose he'd better stay so.'

Declan kissed her. 'You're wonderful and Katie will be thrilled.'

'Before we tell her, though, I think we should get him checked out, Declan. He could be carrying all sorts of diseases.'

'Good idea. He probably needs some routine shots anyway. This will cost us, though. Maybe even fifty or sixty quid,' Declan hazarded.

'Expensive mutt.'

'Still, it will be good for the kids to have a dog around.'

Trish smiled. 'Yeah, I must admit I like the idea of them spending more time outdoors. Katie usually wants to spend all her time playing on the computer, but this week she's hardly asked at all.'

Declan reached down to scratch behind the dog's ear. 'Okay, Hopper, it's a visit to the vet for you tomorrow. And then you can become an official member of the Ryan Family.'

'So you're keeping him?' Viv couldn't hide her delight.

Trish cradled the phone against her shoulder as she ironed her best skirt for the visit to the spa next week. 'Yes, I know, I can't believe it myself. What on earth am I letting myself in for?'

Viv laughed. 'You'll love having him about. Dogs are wonderful company.'

'I have plenty of company, Viv, I can assure you.'

'Ah, yes, but dogs don't answer you back and they eat whatever you put in front of them.'

'You have a point.'

'I'll drop over at the weekend and teach you how to train him. It's very important that a dog knows who's boss, especially in a house with small children.'

'Thanks, Viv, you're a doll.'

The vet looked at Declan over his glasses, his expression grim. 'This animal is in a disgraceful condition and probably in a lot of pain.'

Declan gaped back. 'Well he does look a bit of a mess,

and of course there's the limp but he seems happy enough.'

The vet shot him a look of disdain. 'I don't think so.'

'I'm sorry I don't know much about dogs. Our little girl brought him home last week and though we've put up notices we haven't been able to locate the owner. We thought we might keep him but my wife wanted to get him checked out first. We have very young children and she's afraid he might be carrying some bugs.'

The vet's demeanour changed completely. 'Oh, I see. Well, your wife is a sensible woman. Hopper needs delousing and it would be wise to castrate him too.'

Declan winced. 'Okay.'

'But,' the vet continued, 'I'm afraid it's his leg that concerns me most.'

'It's not good news, Trish,' Declan said when he came home. 'Poor old Hopper is in a bad way.'

'What is it?' Trish immediately went to get the dog some water and a couple of the dog biscuits she'd bought that morning. 'There you go Hopper,' she patted his head before turning questioning eyes on her husband.

'His leg is fractured in several places. The vet suspects he's been mistreated.'

'The poor dog. But can't they fix it?'

'Yes, but it will cost.'

'How much?' Trish asked.

'How *much*?' Viv asked when Trish repeated the figure to her friend.

'I know. Look, don't say anything in front of the kids,' Trish hissed before leading her friend through to the garden.

Katie ran to hug her godmother. 'Viv! Come and meet Hopper.'

Viv bent to pet the dog. 'So this is the famous Hopper. Hello fella.'

'Isn't he wonderful?' Katie's eyes shone with pride.

'My doggy,' Sam announced.

'Bow-wow!' Georgie crawled over to Hopper and yanked his tail.

'No, Georgie, no!' Declan groaned. 'Dear God, the dog will bite your hand off if you do that again.'

'Hello, Georgie boy.' Viv lifted the baby on to her lap and kissed him. 'I think he's safe enough Declan. Hopper seems like a very placid, gentle little dog.'

'A perfect family pet?' Trish murmured. 'Come inside for a cuppa and I'll fill you in on the latest in our shaggy dog story.'

As they waited for the kettle to boil, Trish told Viv about Hopper's leg. 'Apparently it's fractured in a few places and that's why the operation is so expensive. The vet said we should take some time to think about it. He gave Declan the number of an animal rescue centre and he says if we don't want him, they'll take him in.'

'Do the children know?'

Trish shook her head. 'They think we're still trying to find the owner.'

'So what are you going to do?'

'I know Declan would love to keep Hopper as he's almost as nuts about him as the kids are, but he says it's out of the question. We can't afford to pay for his treatment.'

'It's a pity but he's probably right, I mean, what else can you do?'

Trish's eyes met Viv's over her mug. 'Cancel the trip to the spa?'

Viv stared at her open-mouthed. 'Oh but Babes, you've been living for that break!'

Trish shrugged. 'What the hell? We can do it some other time – maybe on my fortieth?'

'Oh, Trish.'

'Do you mind, Viv?'

'Of course I don't mind! I'm lost in admiration for you. You're a great mum and a wonderful human being.'

'And every time I step in poo in my garden I'll regret this decision,' Trish laughed.

'You won't,' Viv assured her.

'I can't remember a time before Hopper, can you?' Viv asked as they sat on the patio two months later, sipping ice-cold lemonade and watching the children play. Georgie, who had just learned to walk, tottered around behind his brother and sister, giggling uncontrollably every time he fell down. Hopper trotted over to him every so often and gave him an encouraging lick.

'No, he's definitely one of the family now,' Trish agreed. 'What I find amazing is how protective he is of the kids, especially Georgie. And he's had a wonderful influence on Katie. She's really taking the whole pet business very seriously and insists on brushing Hopper's coat at least once a week.'

Viv sighed. 'He looks like a different dog to the one I met a couple of months ago.' Hopper's eyes were bright, his coat was shiny and he was flying around as he played with the children, with no evidence of a limp.

'Yes, he's getting quite plump, I may have to put him on a diet!'

'So,' Viv smiled at her friend. 'No regrets?'

Trish shook her head. 'I admit I occasionally dream of that spa break in Wicklow, but when you think about it, that would have been just two days of pleasure for me whereas Hopper makes us all happy every day. It's like having a friend, companion and a wonderful babysitter in the house. I think, when it comes down to it, I got a pretty good deal.'

Patricia Scanlan's novels include *Double Wedding*, *Mirror Mirror*, *City Girl*, *City Woman*, *Promises Promises*, *Francesca's Party*, *Finishing Touches*, *Two for Joy*, *Winter Blessings* and *Divided Loyalties*.

25. HOPE AND JOY
Patricia Scanlan

My two little cats, Hope and Joy, came into my life eight years ago at a time when it seemed I had neither hope nor joy. I was going through a very difficult time physically, emotionally and spiritually. I was staying in my mobile home in Wicklow and had been having a cup of tea over in my sister's. I came back to the mobile to find two little kittens curled up on the settee. One was jet black, the other black and white. I didn't know what to do. I'd never had pets and wasn't mad about cats. I called on the cavalry – my sister, sister-in-law, a plethora of nieces and a nephew.

'Oh Tricia, you have to keep them!'

'I'm not keeping them . . . I don't know anything about cats.'

'Tricia you have to . . . we'll mind them when you can't.'

'Absolutely not . . . I have to travel to publicise my books. They'll need to go to vets and things.'

'We'll feed them. We'll bring them to the vet.'

An excited chorus assaulted my ears as they picked the kittens up and petted the tiny little things. 'I'm calling this one Hope,' my eldest niece who was thirteen at the time, announced as she cuddled the little black one.

I took the little black and white one, looked at her and

heard myself say 'well if that's Hope we'd better call this one Joy.'

On that beautiful sunny summer morning Hope and Joy entered my life. They were abandoned kittens, three months old and sisters, according to the vet I brought them to the next day for a check up and injections.

We went on a spending spree for cat nests, a scratching pole, food and water dishes, toys to play with and the litter tray. I felt if I was going to take on such responsibility, I had to do it properly. I got used to emptying the litter trays, (the nieces weren't quite as enthusiastic about that particular duty) and gradually fell in love.

The kittens both had quite distinctive personalities. Joy was a queen. She'd stalk around imperiously and allowed only so much petting. Hope plodded but she adored cuddling and would purr like a train. Eventually the summer was over and it was time to go home to Dublin and real life. The two of them were so small they fitted into the one cat cage. Snuggling in together, they promptly fell asleep.

I got a cat flap installed and put the little magnetic straps around their necks. The straps drove them mad. Miss Hope nearly strangled herself while Miss Joy ended up with her paw through it, however she managed it. I took off the straps and left them to their own devices and they were fine.

They were good little cats. I had a serious talk with them and told them that the rules of the house included no walking on kitchen counters, tables or mantelpieces. And when the Christmas tree was up, if they so much as went near a bauble, they would be barred to the utility room for the duration of the festivities. They certainly took it to heart as they behaved impeccably with manners a mother could be proud of.

After six months it was time for their operations. I remember feeling so anxious as I dropped them both into the vet and was told to collect them that evening. The relief of getting them home was enormous, even though they staggered around for a while before falling asleep on my lap.

They were very well-informed cats and always watched the news with me. I'd lie on the sofa and they'd lie on my tummy and often the three of us would fall asleep and wake ourselves up snoring. Soon I could not remember my life without them. If I was out for the day the two of them would be perched on top of the garage to greet me when I got home. We went to Wicklow every summer and they would loll on the deck beside me, purring ecstatically.

This summer, my little darling Hope died. A tom cat bit her. I took her to the vet twice. The second time she was put on a drip and I never slept a wink that night. The following morning I got the call to say that she had died.

I'm crying as I write this now because I grieve the loss of my little companion so profoundly. She was the most loving little cat. She was the one who would sit on my knee even when I was trying to write. All Hope wanted was to be cuddled and she was happy.

Whatever room I went into, she always followed and sat with me. Although I still have her sister, I miss Hope more than I ever thought possible. I'd give anything to see her run in to me with her tail as high as it always was.

We all cried and grieved, and we all went in to say our last goodbye to her in the vets. She looked beautiful, as if she were fast asleep, her black coat thick and glossy, her paws curled up under her. They gave us a room to ourselves and my cavalry, who are always with me through thick and thin. We patted her and told her we loved her. The children were so loving and my three-year-old niece demanded to know why Mary, Yvonne and myself had 'water dripping out of our eyes.'

Their grief was a comfort to me. Hope was a much loved cat, not just by me, but by all the extended family. There was a little café next door so we decided we should have refreshments after the 'funeral'. It was so nice, as we all discussed what had happened and our own particular memories of Hope. The others were so earnest in trying to comfort me by telling me she was with Holy God, although Maria in her innocence, felt Hope had just 'gone on holidays to Heaven' and would be back soon.

My memories are of her galloping down the garden with her tail as high as a kite when I rattled her food. Or else curled up on my knee purring so contentedly she sounded as if she was going to burst. People who don't realise the bond that can build up between you and a pet say in a well meaning way 'you should get another.' But all you pet lovers know that it's impossible to substitute one for another. She was the most loving and giving little cat and for me Hope is irreplaceable.

Claudia Carroll's books include
The Last of the Great Romantics,
He Loves Me . . . He Loves Me Not,
Remind Me Again Why I Don't Need A Man
and *I Never Fancied Him Anyway*

26. PET DISASTERS
Claudia Carroll

IN THE INTERESTS OF ANIMAL WELFARE, WHY I
SHOULD NEVER BE ALLOWED HAVE ANY KIND OF
PET, EVER, AS LONG AS I LIVE.

Please don't get me wrong. It's not that I don't love animals,
I do, it's just that they don't seem to love me back. And I
wouldn't mind, but I even come from an animal-loving
family, where pets are treated as well as, if not better, than
the kids.

My father even had a habit of feeding the dogs leftovers
from his own dinner, i.e. the dogs would eat off the human
plates. As a lifelong hygiene fascist, this naturally made my
tummy do all sorts of funny turns, with the result that my
hard and fast rule to survive was (a) to drink liquids only
or (b) to eat directly from a packet/carton/tin, avoiding all
utensils. This naturally led to all sorts of raised eyebrows
whenever we had visitors. My poor parents, however, insisted
that it was a good idea for each of us kids to have a pet of
some sort, as it helped foster a spirit of responsibility and
conscientiousness in us. Or so the theory went . . .

Toby – pet disaster number one.

Toby was a gorgeous, stunning, sweet-natured Airedale Terrier and I loved him so much, he was even allowed sleep in my bed. I was given Toby for my sixth birthday and no first-time mother ever fussed or fretted as much. The only fly in the ointment was my older brother, Richard's pet . . . a fang-toothed, scary-looking Alsatian with the very inappropriate name of Mrs Fluffles. Now this mutt was so high-maintenance that if she was reincarnated as a human, she'd have to be either Cher or Barbra Streisland. Anyway, to say that Mrs Fluffles took an instant dislike to poor Toby is an understatement. I remember coming downstairs one morning and finding clumps of hair and dog teeth strewn all over the kitchen floor. Yes, their fights were that vicious. 'Give it time,' my mother would gently urge, 'they'll get used to each other.'

Horrible brother Richard, however, who at the age of eight was already showing a strong Dell Boy Trotter entrepreneurial streak, had other ideas. Without telling anybody, he took poor, unsuspecting Toby off for a walk one day and sold him to a school mate for the princely sum of two pounds. He came home, pockets stuffed with sweets and comics paid for with his windfall and casually informed my mother not to bother buying so much dog food in the future. Could you even make it up?

Anyway, to save me many years recounting this on psychiatrists' couches, Mom and Dad did the only decent thing any parent could do in similar circumstances. They went out and bought me another terrier, who looked and sounded just like Toby and blithely tried to pass it off as the same dog. Given my youth, they would have probably got away with it, except that this new Toby-look-alike had an utterly different character to the original. Whereas old Toby was sweet natured, cute and affectionate, this one was aggressive, bad-tempered and bit me so badly I spent a whole summer covered in stinky antiseptic cream which attracted wasps and made me smell worse than low tide in Calcutta.

I was well into my teens when my parents eventually confessed and told me about the switch. Up until then, I just thought all dogs were prone to severe personality changes.

Sampson and Delilah the goldfish – pet disaster number two.

After the Toby debacle I gave up on all canine creatures for a while. Instead I splashed out on an aquarium with my Confirmation money. It sounds posh, but it was really just a very large fish tank full of furry stones and plastic mermaids from Hector Greys. I put it in pride of place in our living room, beside the telly, where I could admire Sampson and Delilah all day long.

One dull, rainy evening, when there was nothing on TV but an episode of *Little House on the Prairie*, my gaze happened to fall on the aquarium. Sampson was eating Delilah. Whole. In one big gulp. I was stunned and disgusted. Not only did that spell the end of any further association with aquatic pets, I haven't even eaten fish since. Euughhhh . . .

Gnasher – pet disaster number three.

Don't let the name fool you, Gnasher was actually a lovely black cat. I named him after Denis the Menace's dog in the

Beano. At the time I was in my twenties, sharing a house with my two best friends and having a great laugh. Except that the other two girls hated, and I really mean hated, poor Gnasher. I'd had a feeling they weren't exactly what you might call cat-lovers, but I had taken Gnasher from a friend of mine when her cat had kittens and had hoped my pals would also fall in love with this little cute black furry ball. No such luck.

Now at the time, Karen, my flatmate and best friend, ran a successful language school and she always, always dressed the part. While myself and Susan, our other friend and flatmate, went around dressed like Kurt Cobain's sidekick and P Diddy's girlfriend respectively, Karen was always immaculate in Hermes scarves, Chanel suits and Queen Mother-style handbags.

Anyway, Karen's very understandable grievance against Gnasher, was that he used to swing out of her Woolford tights when she hung them over the back of radiators to dry. Consequently, her weekly tights bill was coming in at over a whopping hundred quid!

Susan's grievance was a tad more serious as Gnasher happened to give her ringworm. I knew he had it, but I guessed the others wouldn't react favourably if they found out, so I secretly smuggled him off to the vet one day. The vet diagnosed him, gave me fungicidal cream to put on his little nose and told me to ask my long-suffering flatmates to watch out for any suspicious roundy-looking marks on their skin. Ringworm, of course, is highly contagious to humans.

Too late. Eagle-eyed Karen demanded to know what the suspicious-looking cream was on Gnasher.

'Cat anti-wrinkle cream,' I lied.

It was too late for poor Susan though, who ended up on a course of antibiotics to clear up her ringworm.

"I've enough difficulty getting a boyfriend," she screamed at me, "without ringworm adding to my troubles."

At this point I knew that poor Gnasher's days were well and truly numbered . . .

Like Lord Lucan or Shergar, the mystery of Gnasher's eventual disappearance has never been satisfactorily solved. There had been a building site right across the road from us, and he'd made friends with all the workmen. He'd even sit with them when they were having their tea breaks. All was well until the foreman called to our house one day to say he'd found Gnasher asleep in the cement mixer. He asked me to take better care of him. No negligent mother ever felt as guilty as I did after that stinging rebuke. But not even saucers of the most expensive cat food could stop him from wandering across to visit his new pals on the building site.

And one day, he just never came home. Karen and Susan, although both secretly delighted at this unexpected turn of events, did help put up posters all around the greater Lansdowne Park area. 'Have you seen this cat?' read the message.

I spent weeks going around the house bawling, but he never showed. Now, every time I drive down Lansdowne Park, and look at the new townhouses, I wonder whether he fell asleep in the cement mixer. Did Gnasher somehow end up in the foundations of all those new houses? Is that where my cute little cat is interred?

And then I remind myself that the kindest thing that I can do for any poor, defenceless animal, is never, ever to own one.

Members of the ISPCA can sleep easy . . .

Evan Fanning is a
Sunday Independent journalist.

27. JACK
Evan Fanning

My dog died recently. It's very difficult to explain quite how much this affects you. You tell yourself it's only a dog but then spend days wandering around in a daze, watching people scooping up dog shit thinking they don't know how lucky they are. I should start by saying that he was our family dog, but mainly hung out with my younger brother, with whom he developed an almost telepathic understanding.

His name was Jack, and when we acquired him we were warned that he felt his standing in the world to be far greater than someone who is only eighteen inches tall, can't speak and is willing to jump for food, could normally expect to be.

We quickly realised that although Jack had many of the traits that you would normally associate with a dog, we couldn't be entirely confident that he was one. We were aware that he was a mongrel of some kind but beyond that it was hard to be more specific. He appeared to be a Jack Russell – his name was Jack so we guessed the rest – but he had a mane of golden hair just like a lion. He could snap like a crocodile and had a white Mohican like that Gremlin who spoke with the posh accent.

He would never chase anything and at first we tried hard.

We'd coax him into the garden, which was always more difficult than it should have been, throw a stick and wait for him to run after it. Jack would look up at you with a patronising expression that said, "Well done. You can throw a stick. Was that really worth waking me up for?" before heading back inside to resume his nap. Tennis balls were met with the same reaction. The only thing he ever came close to running after was a Brussels sprout one Christmas. He could see the point in chasing that.

Within days of his arrival Jack had effectively taken over the house. He would eat anything and was one the laziest individuals, human or otherwise, I'd ever come across. At night he would find his way into your bed while you were asleep and lie down under the covers with his head on the pillow. At some point you'd wake up and realise that you were now sleeping in a six inch space at the edge of the mattress, while Jack lay in a space far too great for a dog of his meagre size. If you tried to address the situation he'd have no hesitation in biting you.

On walks he'd start fights with dogs five times his size and then walk off leaving you to fend off an angry combination of Alsatian and owner. He had a thing for minorities. I think he sensed some vulnerability. When a boy in a wheelchair – whose legs and wheels your dog has just been gnawing at – suggests your dog should be locked up, and the only thing you can think of to say is, "Ah, *you* should be locked up," then you realise you've signed up to more than just owning a pet. What you've got on your hands is a political movement, and in our case, an extreme right wing one. But what choice do you have? With a wag of his tail and a friendly welcome, he won us over. So we signed up to whatever he had to offer. Fat kids, postmen, other dogs, Cork people, homosexuals. Jack hated them all. The gay men was a particularly interesting one. We could never figure quite how he identified them from his vantage point but he managed it somehow. It must be in the shoes.

We realised his true colours on a trip to a relation's farm in the country. Like all farms they had a lovely, but lively sheepdog. Despite the fact we knew Jack hated all other dogs, it felt deeply wrong to leave him sitting in the car on a baking hot day when the open fields and streams of the farm lay waiting for him. We were also sure that he himself would rather stay sleeping in the car, but we felt we knew better despite the presence of the other dog.

Without the security of being on his lead, and perhaps realising that he was not going to be dragged to safety by his owners, Jack behaved reasonably well while on the farm. It would be way too strong a sentiment to say that he became friends with the sheepdog, but he tolerated his presence as a youngster would to a second cousin a few years his junior.

After a couple of peaceful hours we said goodbye and left their house. They all came out to wave us off, including their dog. As soon as Jack was safely back in the car he began a frantic attempt to attack the sheepdog he had so admirably tolerated earlier, by jumping at the window and barking like a maniac. Once he realised his chances of getting hurt were slim to none he had gone on the offensive. That was a revealing day. As we drove off he gave us an apologetic look. I think he realised what we had all seen.

In an effort to prove us wrong he effectively doubled his attack rate when we took him for walks. It eventually became so perilous that in the end we discovered it was safer to just stay in the house and let Jack patrol the windowsill, keeping one eye out for neighbours he didn't like and the other on the TV where, with relish, he would attack any dog that appeared on the screen.

Each day he would tear the post to shreds as it arrived – his version of the Nazi book burning – and then strut back in to the living room with an expression on his face that said, "I bet you're glad I'm here now."

However, with a dog, things like being a daft racist become character traits and Jack provided us with constant entertainment. There were also lots of things he did like, such as Tayto cheese and onion crisps, grapes, prawn crackers and sleeping. He could jump higher than anyone I've ever seen, provided there was some food on offer, and on this front would never let you down on the big occasions when you had visitors and wanted to show off.

He developed first bronchitis and then pancreatitis, afflictions normally associated with chronic smokers and alcoholics, and ultimately had to be put down. We buried him in the garden with a packet of Tayto crisps.

Jack would hate it but I think we'll have to get a new dog soon. The void is too big as it is. So if you know of anyone trying out some strange cross breeding techniques that at least in some way involve a Jack Russell, please do let me know. The minorities of Dublin have had it easy for too long.

Mary Malone is the author of *Love Match* and *All You Need is Love*.

www.marymalone.info

28. FOOTPRINTS IN THE SNOW
Mary Malone

I looked into his unknowing eyes as we lay side by side on the soft flannel sheets, the heavy blankets snuggled around us keeping our naked bodies warm. The falling sleet and snow rapped noisily against the cold window pane. I loved looking out at it, revelling in the magic of Christmas and all its promise. He liked it too. We'd had so many Christmas mornings like this together. He'd sit patiently, waiting for me to open both his presents and mine, watching my every move as I'd slowly peel the colourful wrapping from the secret gifts.

We'd been together for quite a few years, you see, but now things were about to change. Sighing, I realised there was no easy way to tell him this – some things just couldn't be dressed up in fancy wrapping paper. We had been best friends long before we moved in together, making a most unlikely pair. He was as blonde as I was dark; his eyes chocolate while mine resembled a bright summer sky. I knew others admired his loyalty and I continually tested his patience and love. But he never failed to show it in abundance, no matter how much I hurt him or excluded him when somebody new or more interesting appeared.

I pulled the sheets over my face, cringing with shame at

my deliberate attempts to push him away. A sharp pain gripped my abdomen, forcing me to grab him tightly as I waited for the tightness to subside. He patted my hand soothingly, sensing my discomfort. I couldn't quite comprehend the extent of his kindness. Guilt suffused me. What kind of a girl was I? How could I be so mean?

'I'm really sorry,' I suddenly blurted out. 'I can't put you first anymore. Somebody else is arriving very soon.'

I looked away from him then, unable to watch while doubt clouded his eyes. He seemed to be listening closely, aware of the changing tone of my voice. Dawn was near and the dark sky had broken into portions of grey cloud, the moon receding behind the fluffy moving shapes.

He remained silent, no doubt waiting for me to continue. It had always been the same. He listened carefully while I did all the talking, leaning his head to one side until I'd finished. This time seemed different, however, and I sensed him ease his body ever so slightly away from mine. Male instinct, I guessed. Yet another wave of pain gripped me as an invisible distance grew between us. Who could blame him for pulling away?

I reached out to touch him, placing a finger on his warm lips, smiling as he relented slightly and his tongue gently licked the tip of my finger, tickling the palm of my hand as it flickered against my warm skin.

'You tease,' I laughed then, as a mischievous grin appeared in his eyes, dissolving the tension-filled air. 'Don't be nice to me. It'll only make this more difficult for both of us. I don't have a choice. I'm begging you to understand.'

I clutched the blankets tightly, waiting for another sharp ache to pass. His sensual touch immediately lightened the atmosphere in the room, and I stole the opportunity to sidle a bit nearer to him and feel his warm breath on my face. I was anxious to get as much as I could from our last few moments together. But then, I had always been a taker, while he was content to give in to my every whim. And though I was about to hurt him again, I hoped that in time he'd become accustomed to the change, and that he'd wait in the shadows for the moment to arrive when I would undoubtedly welcome him home again.

'I'm getting up,' I said finally as daylight filled the room. I was very nervous, I realised with a pang. Too nervous to risk letting my old loyal playmate cross paths with my latest love.

Keeping my back firmly to him, I slipped my feet into cushioned slippers and padded into the adjoining bathroom, silently willing him to have gone before I returned. I stared at my blotchy face in the mirror. My dark hair was a mess and its natural shine was absent that Christmas morning. I decided to jump in the shower. Pain or no pain, I couldn't leave the house without at least freshening up. There was a lot to do and very little time to do it in.

As the warm water cascaded down my back and shoulders, I allowed myself the liberty to look ahead to my future. Shivering with excitement, and my teeth chattering, I contemplated our first meeting. Nothing could ever compare to the sensuous thrill of that initial chemical attraction.

I pushed open the window to release the steam from the small bathroom, peeping through the tiny opening towards the ground below and smiling in relief when I saw his footprints in the snow. I caught a last glimpse of him in the distance, just before he disappeared around the front of the house and out to the icy road.

Stopping to catch my breath as another dart of pain shot

across my body, I inhaled slowly to calm the nerves inside me. I'd always guessed it would be painful, but nothing could have prepared me for this heart-wrenching ordeal.

A short while later I felt more relaxed and returned to the bedroom to dress. The room was filled with his strong scent. I decided not to waste another moment on the past and immediately began tugging at the blankets until they lay on the floor in a crumpled pile. The warmth had long since left the flannel sheets and I swept them roughly into another bundle before dropping them directly into the laundry chute.

Another pain, this time lasting a lot longer, left me little choice but to pace up and down the cold wooden floor in my satin underwear. A lonely ray of Christmas cheer, I thought with wry humour, as the weak winter sun made its first appearance of the day. I hid my nakedness from view as I peeped around the curtain to take in the magnificent sight of the forest in the distance. Snow weighed heavily on the branches, but their beauty failed to hold my attention as my eyes scanned the ground for new footprints in the fresh blanket of snow. There were none.

Fifteen minutes later, I was driving away from home, still in pain, but feeling more upbeat now and much more concerned about what lay ahead rather than what I'd left behind. I pushed the accelerator harder with my right foot, wishing I had a hand to hold or a shoulder to lean on. Checking the rear view mirror as I reversed into a parking spot, I was surprised to notice the beads of perspiration on my brow.

I concentrated on my steps as I trod carefully on the icy path towards the front door of the building, glancing disinterestedly at the brightly-lit Christmas tree standing in the centre of the entrance hall. Festive music played softly in the background and bon-bon dishes overflowed with mouth-watering chocolates. Within seconds, a friendly face appeared at my side.

'Merry Christmas. What a beautiful day for new beginnings. Are you ready?'

'Definitely,' I nodded, accepting the proffered arm. 'I don't think I can wait much longer.'

'No point standing around here then,' my companion grinned.

The next few hours passed in a light-headed blur and then the moment I'd been waiting for finally arrived, the best Christmas present ever. He burst into my life with refreshing energy. Within minutes his head lay on my bare chest and I fell instantly in love. We lay there together, happy to stare into each other's eyes, oblivious to all the activity around us. I stroked his damp hair and counted his tiny fingers and toes.

'My beautiful son,' I whispered. 'I can't wait to take you home and show you the luscious green forests and the clear blue sky.'

As he nuzzled my neck, my fingers spanned his perfect spine and supported his delicate head, smiling as he pushed against me. His lips moved against my skin and I was reminded of the one I'd pushed away that morning, wondering if perhaps I could have handled things differently. Could I have risked having both of them in my life after all?

Christmas passed quickly but the snow remained long into the springtime. The baby and I fell into an easy routine, eating and sleeping or relaxing in front of a blazing fire.

'Look at the snow,' I told him, shielding his dark eyes

from the strong glare, and laughing as he kicked his legs excitedly as a red-breasted robin perched beside us on the window ledge.

The baby's eyes grew accustomed to the brightness outside and he focused on the unfamiliar shapes and movements around him, reaching out his arms to touch. As we explored the garden further, strolling towards the front of the house, I stopped abruptly when I noticed new footprints in the snow. Glancing around this way and that, I couldn't understand how they'd appeared without my noticing. Hastening my step, I followed the footprints step by step, disappointed when their trail faded on the thawed roadway.

'Did you see those prints?' I said out loud, much to the amusement of the baby, who happily gurgled in reply. 'How come we didn't hear anything or catch a glimpse of any movement?'

I shook my head in disbelief, afraid to hope or dream it could be him checking on us. Maybe there would be a chance for the three of us after all? My heart leapt with anticipation.

The snow melted quickly in the following days, the temperatures slowly increasing to above normal. I scanned the melting slush for any traces of footprints, wondering if I'd somehow imagined them, allowing my fantasies to play tricks on me.

When the last of the snow had disappeared, my baby and I sat by the creek and watched the fish rise to the surface after a long cold winter. I caught a sudden movement out of the corner of my eye, and turned quickly to check what it was. And there he stood before me. A lump rose in my throat when I saw him and I immediately turned the baby around to let him catch a glimpse of our visitor. I whispered soothingly in his ear, letting him know it was okay and there was nothing to fear. My fears were unfounded however. The baby gurgled with joy as the beautiful golden Labrador wagged his tail excitedly and bounded towards us, coming to a sudden stop at my feet. I put my hand out to rub his head lovingly.

'I'm sorry I was mean to you again, but I was afraid you might be jealous of the baby.'

He looked at me then, cocking his head to the side in his quirky way, as if to ask why.

'I know you think I'm crazy and I can't say I blame you,' I laughed. 'Come on, let's get you something to eat and get you in out of the cold.'

All this time the baby was perched safely on my hip, fascinated by the dog's every movement. He padded along beside me as we left the creek and made our way back to the house. He then waited patiently outside while I retrieved his bowl from the back of the press and prepared him a welcome home feast.

Though it took a while for us to develop a new routine and establish some necessary ground rules, the three of us are doing well together now. My earlier fears have completely evaporated. My beloved son and dog have now bonded so well that I sometimes feel like the one out in the cold. Though his footprints in the snow have long since disappeared, his loyalty and love are forever imprinted on my heart.

Sarah Webb's books include *Three Times A Lady*, *It Had To Be You*, *Some Kind of Wonderful*, *Something to Talk About*, *Always the Bridesmaid* and *Take a Chance*. Sarah also edited *Travelling Light*, in aid of the Kisiizi Hospital in Uganda.

www.sarahwebb.info

29. THE CATALYST: A FAIRY TALE FOR GROWN-UPS

Sarah Webb

'I'm not bloody going,' Rita said to her sister, Sadie, on Thursday evening. 'I've had a terrible week and hearing about Amanda's oh-so-perfect life will probably send me over the edge. And I bet she'll make us watch her wedding video again.' She groaned. 'I couldn't bear it.'

'It was a lovely wedding all the same,' Sadie said a touch wistfully. 'All that white chiffon and lilies. Very tasteful. But I know what you mean. Anyway, please say you'll come,' she begged. 'I know it's short notice but she really wants to see us. And I've bullied Pat into babysitting. I haven't been out for ages. But I don't think I can cope with Amanda on my own, especially stone cold sober. At least you can drink.'

'True. And she does always serve rather nice wine.'

Sadie laughed. 'And besides,' she continued, 'it's a heavily pregnant woman's prerogative to get her own way. Think of what we have to put up with – swollen ankles, huge breasts, heart burn, morning sick . . .'

'Enough, enough. I'll come, OK? Although the bit about the huge breasts doesn't sound too bad if you ask me.'

'Great.' Sadie was delighted. 'I'll pick you up at seven.'

As soon as Amanda opened the door, Rita knew she'd made a mistake. The hall smelt of oranges, one of Amanda's expensive Jo Malone candles no doubt. Amanda chose her own presents every birthday and Christmas (she hated clutter, and unwanted presents which ended up in a charity shop, were, in her opinion, a waste of money). Last December she had asked Rita and Sadie to buy her some Jo Malone 'stuff' in Brown Thomas, Dublin's most exclusive department store and Amanda's favourite shop. They'd only been able to afford a candle.

'Come in, come in,' Amanda gushed, folding her arms over her chest and rubbing each upper arm with the opposite hand. 'Isn't it cold out there? I've had the heating on all day.'

Rita and Sadie followed her into the immaculate living room after handing over their coats. They sank down into the huge velvet cream sofa, the feather cushions sighing under their combined weight. Rita folded her hands on her lap and Sadie rearranged the scattered cushions behind her back to give her some support.

'So how are the kids, Sadie?' Amanda asked, sitting opposite them in a matching cream oversized armchair. She was wearing a slim-fitting sky-blue cashmere jumper which reeked 'designer'.

'Great, thanks.' Sadie tried not to worry. She wasn't used to such squashy cushions under her bum (the very finest goose feathers apparently) and with the extra weight of the baby pressing down she felt a little at sea. She hoped she could get off the sofa when the time came. She might have to ask Rita to pull her up. And what if her waters broke? Amanda would never forgive her for ruining the sofa.

'And how's work, Rita?' Amanda continued. 'Still writing about make-up?'

'Yes,' Rita answered through gritted teeth. Rita was the health and beauty correspondent for *Woman's Way* magazine and loved her job. 'And it's going well, thanks. And how is little Ollie?'

'Oliver,' Amanda corrected her. 'Owen doesn't like Ollie. He's fine.' Oliver was Amanda and Owen's six month old baby, a dote of a thing with huge Bambi brown eyes and a shock of the darkest black hair. Even Rita adored him and she wasn't exactly a baby person.

'Good.'

They all looked at each other for a moment, no one quite sure what to say next.

Amanda broke the awkward atmosphere by jumping to her feet and clapping her hands together. 'Right, let's eat.'

Rita looked at Amanda. She was being a little odd. Nervy, Rita thought. Her sister's face seemed even thinner than usual, more pinched if that was possible, and her left eye seemed to flicker a little after she blinked.

Sadie pushed herself forwards towards the edge of the sofa and then levered herself up with her hands.

'Are you OK?' Rita asked her.

'Just about.'

They followed Amanda into the kitchen.

'Just pasta I'm afraid,' Amanda trilled. 'And some salads I threw together. And I made some tomato bread last night when Oliver was asleep.'

'Sounds lovely,' Sadie said. 'You know me, I'll eat anything.'

Amanda shot her a look.

'Not that this is just anything,' Sadie added, kicking herself.

'You shouldn't have gone to such trouble,' Rita said. 'You're very good.'

'No trouble at all,' Amanda shrugged. She walked towards the berry-red double Aga and began to stir the contents of a copper-based top of the range saucepan. 'And we're starting with pan seared scallops. I hope you like them.'

'Lovely,' Sadie murmured.

Rita was gobsmacked. 'Where do you find the time? Were you not working today?'

Amanda worked as a nurse in a private and exclusive IVF clinic on Fitzwilliam Square which specialised in older mothers.

'I was,' she said. 'I shopped on the Internet last night and it was delivered this afternoon. I only work till four as you know.'

'Eight until four,' Rita pointed out. 'A full day.'

After a long pause, Amanda asked Rita to take the wine out of the fridge. 'It's from New Zealand, I hope you like it.'

'Lovely,' Rita said, following Amanda's instructions. Turning to Sadie she offered her a glass.

'Go on, it won't kill me,' Sadie said. 'But just one, mind.'

An hour and a half, and two bottles of wine later, Amanda suggested they adjourn to the drawing room.

'Drawing room,' Rita snorted. 'This is Blackrock, Amanda, not London. And it's a modern semi-d, not a Georgian mansion.'

Amanda glared at her and was about to open her mouth to say something cutting about Rita's tiny one bedroom flat but Sadie cut in.

'Have you been decorating again?' she asked Amanda quickly, looking around, eager to keep her sisters from sniping at each other. 'Something's different.'

'The curtains,' Amanda said, taking a large gulp of wine. It was going down rather too easily. Rita seemed to be having the same problem. 'They arrived last week. The fabric's French.'

'And how's Owen?' Sadie continued.

Was it her imagination, Sadie wondered, or did Amanda purse her lips at the mention of her husband's name?

'Owen?' Amanda took another gulp of wine. 'He's never home. He says he has a lot on at work but the truth is he's probably in some hotel shagging his new secretary as we speak.'

Sadie gasped as Rita looked at Amanda in amazement.

'Oh, yes,' Amanda continued. 'Owen's quite the ladies' man, apparently. His PA, Celine, rang me only last night to tell me all about it. Or ex PA I should say, she was let go yesterday. She wasn't too pleased to be dumped for a younger model I can tell you, she's only just turned twenty-six herself. But his new PA is twenty-two apparently and how did Celine describe her? Oh yes, "legs up to her armpits and hot to trot".'

'I had no idea,' Sadie said. 'I don't know what to say. I'm so sorry.'

Amanda waved her hand dismissively. 'Don't be sorry. He's a prick. Always has been. Serves me right for marrying money.'

Rita stifled a laugh.

'Oh, go ahead, Rita,' Amanda said. 'Laugh all you like. It's true. And I've certainly got my comeuppance, haven't I? I'm sure you're just delighted, Rita. Go on, admit it.'

'I am actually,' Rita said. She raised her glass as if to toast Amanda. 'Glad to see your life is just as fucked up as the rest of us mere mortals.'

'Rita!' Sadie was shocked.

'No, she's right,' Amanda said. 'I've been insufferable, I know that. But it's become a bit of a habit now I'm afraid, this bloody way of life. I don't know who I am anymore. We both work all hours to pay for this mausoleum of a house and for what? So that someone else can raise our child? So that we can replace our cars whenever we feel like it? So that we can redecorate the whole house every year? Take foreign holidays to places like Antigua where you leave the compound, only to feel guilty as hell at the poverty of the place?' Amanda was on a roll. 'I'm sick of it all but I can't see an end to it.'

'So give me your car,' Rita said. 'Leave work and look after Oliver instead. And I'm sure Sadie and her gang would love to go somewhere hot. You could stay at home and give them your tickets. Hey, you can even donate some money to charity if it makes you feel any better.'

'Rita!' Sadie said again.

Rita ignored her. 'It's easy for you to complain about your life, Amanda. Yes, your husband is having an affair, big swing. He'll never leave you, it wouldn't be good for his image. And you like your comfortable lifestyle too much to do anything about changing. Admit it.'

'And your life is perfect, isn't it?' Amanda said with a sneer.

'Never said it was.'

'No, you just go on and on about how bad it is instead,' Amanda pointed out. 'We're polar opposites. At least I take responsibility for my life. You spend your time blaming everyone else for everything bad that happens to you. That's worse.'

'I do not!' Rita said, getting cross.

'Yes, you do. You blame your failed love life on the lack of decent men in Dublin.'

'That one's true.'

'And you didn't get the editor's job in that new magazine because the woman interviewing you didn't like blondes.'

'Also true,' Rita added. She didn't like the direction this conversation was taking.

'And you blame your lack of self-confidence on your upbringing. Well I don't suffer from any lack of self esteem and I'm your sister.'

'But you're the eldest!' Rita spluttered. 'I'm the middle sibling. It's a documented fact that middle siblings are at a disadvantage.'

'What are youngest siblings supposed to be like?' Sadie asked with interest.

Rita and Amanda both ignored her.

'And why haven't you written that book yet?' Amanda continued. '*The Irish Beauty Bible*? The one you've been going on about for the last five years. Why don't you get your finger out and actually write the damn thing.'

'Actually Amanda, for your information, I sent a few chapters to a publisher only last month.'

'And?' Amanda demanded.

'They said it wasn't quite right for them and also that it needed more work.'

'Ha!' Amanda said.

'Ha, what?'

'So you're not going to bother finishing it now, are you?'

'There's not much point if it's not right for them, is there?'

'Jeez, Rita, they're one publisher in hundreds.' Amanda shook her head. 'You always give up so easily.'

'And you've always been a bossy old cow. Leave me alone.'

'What an intelligent answer.'

'Amanda! Rita! This is supposed to be a nice, civilised evening. Can't you just be nice to each other?'

'Why?'

'Because you're sisters!'

'You're just as bad,' Rita said, rounding on Sadie. Rita was still smarting from Amanda's comments, all a little too close to the bone for her liking.

'What do you mean?' Sadie was confused. 'What have I done?'

'Nothing!' Rita spat. 'That's just it. You rely on everyone else to do everything for you. No wonder you haven't been out for ages, you never bother to pick up the phone to arrange anything. And you should stop having children that you can't afford. And as for the bloody stray dogs, what was it last count? Four? No wonder your house is always a kip.'

'Rita!' This time it was Amanda's turn to be shocked.

'Don't you start, Amanda. You said the very same thing to me on the phone to me recently.'

Sadie was practically in tears. 'Why are you being so mean? I like children. I always wanted a big family, and luckily Pat feels the same way. I shouldn't have to defend my choice. And the kids love the dogs. And we only have two, Rita, as well you know. Jonah had to be put down as he never picked up after that traffic accident, poor fellow. Although I'd love more if we could afford to keep them. You wouldn't believe the amount of people who abandon dogs in Wicklow. It's tragic.'

'But you're always in debt, Sadie,' Rita pointed out.

'Only to the bank,' Sadie said. 'Not to anyone that matters.'

Amanda smiled. Rita began to laugh too. 'Sadie!'

'Well, it's true. So what if we owe the bank money? Does it really matter?'

'I suppose not,' Rita said. She'd never really thought about it.

'Why did you ask us here this evening?' Sadie turned to Amanda. 'I know we're related, but we always end up arguing when we're together. And it was even worse when Mum and Dad were alive, remember? Mum had such a sharp tongue, Dad was a bully and I always hated family dinners. Christmas was a verbal bloodbath. Someone always ended up crying, and it was usually me.'

'Before you both storm out, I want to ask you both something.' Amanda stared down at her hands which were clasped in her lap.

'What?' Rita and Sadie were intrigued. They forgot their grievances for a moment and turned their attention to their older sister.

Amanda lifted her head. She had a strange expression on her face. 'I want you to be Oliver's godparents. I want to get him christened. I know he's six months now, and Owen's not religious, he can take it or leave it. But it's important to me.'

'Both of us?' Sadie asked. 'Can you do that? Two sisters as godmothers?'

Amanda nodded. 'Yes. I asked the rector.'

Rita was gobsmacked. 'After everything I've said to you tonight, you still want me to be Ollie's godmother?'

'Yes.'

Rita sat back in the sofa. 'Well,' was all she could manage.

'Why?' Sadie asked. 'Why us? You have loads of friends, Amanda. No offence, but would you not prefer to ask one of them? Lottie Bond-Reilly maybe, or Pamela?'

Amanda snorted. 'Pamela had an affair with Owen. Celine told me. Oh, Celine knows it all. She's kept records of all his shenanigans over the past three years, you see. From before they were together.'

'No!' Rita exclaimed. 'Pamela Maher? You two have been friends since school. Besides, she doesn't seem the type. Are you sure?'

'Oh yes. It just goes to show, you never can tell,' Amanda said. 'What's the expression?'

'It's always the quiet ones?' Rita offered.

'Exactly!'

'Owen and Pamela?' Sadie said shaking her head. 'I still can't believe it.'

Amanda shrugged.

'I'm glad I didn't go out for lunch with him that time,' Rita said. 'Or Celine might have my name on her list.'

'He never asked you!' Sadie shrieked. 'I don't believe it!'

'It's true. The year before last. Just after you lost the baby, Amanda.'

'Bastard!'

'You know,' Sadie said, thinking back, 'he asked me out for lunch once after Ethan was born. But I thought he was just being nice. I'd always wanted to see the government buildings and he offered to show me around. But I don't think he meant anything by it.' Sadie stopped for a moment. 'However, I do remember him saying he could only show one person around at a time. So Pat would have to stay at home. But you don't think . . . not me?'

'Yes! Even you, Sadie.' Amanda gave a scream. 'That man has to be stopped. He's lethal. This is too much. That's it, I've had enough. Owen's going to pay.'

'Do you know something?' Sadie added thoughtfully, 'If he's capable of that kind of behaviour in his private life, who knows what he gets up to when he's running the country. But what can we do?'

'Hit him where it hurts,' Rita said.

'Like in the balls with a golf club?' Sadie suggested.

Rita and Amanda laughed. 'Not quite what I had in mind, Sadie,' Amanda said. 'Something a little more subtle.'

'Do you have Celine's number?' Rita asked.

Amanda nodded. 'What do you have in mind?'

Rita grinned. 'I'm a journalist, remember?'

The Evening Herald Front Page – October 7th 2006

The Taoiseach, Owen O'Reilly, resigned this morning following the public revelation of an extra marital affair by his former PA, Celine Jones. His estranged wife, Amanda O'Reilly, fled the country last week to pursue a nursing career in a Niger hospital, taking her son Oliver with her. 'Amanda has always wanted to make a difference,' the Taoiseach revealed earlier this week.

The Evening Herald has also learned that Ms O' Reilly, a fluent French speaker, recently sold the couple's Dublin home, donating the entire proceeds to the hospital and to her sister Sadie's dog shelter in Wicklow. The Taoiseach is now believed to be residing in a modest two-bedroom apartment in the city centre.

Ms O'Reilly was also accompanied by her sister, Rita Collins, a journalist who will be teaching in the local primary school, attached to the hospital. Speaking from Niger, Ms Collins exclusively told the Evening Herald, 'Owen O'Reilly never deserved my sister. She may have her faults, but she's been a loyal wife and a good mother to Ollie. It's terrible that Celine's revelations had to come out like this, and on Amanda's birthday too.'

Dawn Cairn's books include *Tulips, Chips and Mayonnaise* and *Goose Eggs and Hoover Bags*.

30. BOLD BASIL AND THE BLACK BEAR

Dawn Cairns

"Bas. Stay boy," Tom grunted as he lifted another heavy black rubbish bag out of the boot of his Audi estate car and slung it over his shoulder.

The whining continued however from the back seat, getting steadily louder.

"Basil!" Tom cast an eye back to the car as he carted the bag up the steps to the half-filled cavernous skip at the dump. He breathed a sigh of relief as he tipped the bag over the side and it slumped down into the stinky depths, on top of the other three he had already thrown in.

"Who would have thought a small garden could have so much rubbish?" he muttered to himself as he jogged back down the steps to the car, wiggling his fingers to get the circulation back into them after holding the heavy bags.

Basil, his ill-behaved black Cocker Spaniel was jumping about in the back seat, smudging the windows with his wet nose in a desperate effort to get out and get involved in whatever Tom was doing. He'd made several unsuccessful attempts at clambering into the boot but the dog guard that Tom had earlier fitted, had so far stopped Basil's escape.

"Calm down boy, one more bag and we can go." Tom

pushed his fingers through the bar to the over excited dog and got his hand licked and rubbed with a wet nose as a reward.

Tom heaved the last of the refuse sacks over his right shoulder, cursing mildly under his breath at the muck and grass cuttings the bags had left in his boot. He was half way up the steps at the skip when he heard the unmistakable sound of claws on concrete. The dog guard had finally given way.

"Och Basil!" Tom swung round, unbalancing himself and nearly falling off the steps, just in time to see his two-year-old dog running round the car park of the dump, his stumpy tail wagging double time, and his black shiny body wriggling with the excitement of getting out of the car.

"Very pleased with yourself I'm sure," Tom said as he heaved the last of the garden rubbish into the skip. He wiped his forehead with the back of his hand. All that physical exertion had brought out a tiny string of beaded sweat on his forehead.

For the millionth time he wished he'd stuck at the dog training classes. But Basil had been so mortifying that Tom had slunk off in embarrassment after the dog-treat incident. Basil, unable to grasp the basics of sitting and staying, never mind walking on a lead had managed to open the dog trainer's Tupperware box full of dried liver pieces and devoured them. To add insult to injury he then vomited them all back up in the middle of the class, much to the horror of the all the other new dog owners. He and Basil had felt decidedly unwanted after that by the neat miniature Schnauzers and manicured Shih-Tzus.

Tom had definitely not made any friends and since the vomiting incident he hadn't had the nerve to go back. Even though the girl with the Newfoundland pup was very attractive, and he hadn't noticed a wedding ring on her finger, he couldn't even really remember what colour her hair was. Still, he had been so sure that the Newfoundland would have got on brilliantly with Basil. Oh well . . .

Basil trotted round the bottom of the row of skips, sniffing the myriad of smells that dogs get so excited about.

"Come on Bas, back into the car." Tom stood beside the open boot motioning to Basil to jump in.

As usual, Basil seemed to have lost his hearing. He didn't even lift his head at the sound of his master's voice, his wagging and sniffing continued unabated.

Thankfully the dump wasn't busy and there was only one other car there. It was an old Renault Five and its owner, a white-haired lady, was rummaging in her boot.

"Basil, come here now!" Tom tried to sound firm and in control. The elderly woman, casting unimpressed glances in his direction, climbed the steps to throw out a couple of ancient lamps. Tom was about to offer to climb the wobbling steps for her, when she glared at him.

"People who can't control their dogs, I don't know," she said loudly and looked away from Tom as if he was the very worst of offenders.

Old bag, he thought to himself as she marched back to her car, her head held high with indignation.

Tom looked around for Basil as the old dragon revved her Renault out of the car park, leaving Tom standing in a cloud of blue smoke. The unmistakable smell of burning clutch hung in the air. There was no sign of the dog.

"Oh for Pete's sake, where has he gone to now?" Tom muttered aloud as he checked behind each skip. Basil was nowhere to be found.

Tom strode back to his car, closed the boot and got into the driving seat. He then spent the next twenty minutes driving slowly up and down all the side streets near the dump to make sure Basil wasn't sniffing his way around all the rubbish hot spots. As he drove, Tom's mood shifted from anger to worry. Where on earth could Basil have gone?

Tom walked up a few driveways and rang doorbells. Most people were out as it was 10:30 am on a Tuesday morning so a lot of people would be out at work. At the empty houses, Tom sneaked a look in the back gardens. Basil may have wandered into someone's garden through a hedge or an open gate and got stuck. All the gardens were empty save for a few sets of swings, potted geraniums and dandelions thriving on lawns that needed to be mowed. They reminded Tom of his own garden. He had just moved house – well he and Basil had just moved house, and had inherited a wilderness as a back garden. That's what all the rubbish bags had been for. He'd filled them with grass cuttings, weeds and the remains of a dilapidated garden shed which had fallen down when he had opened the door to peer inside. The house was a fresh start for him and Basil. Since Betty died and Tessa had left, it had taken a while, but Tom was now finally ready to get on with his life.

Betty had been Basil's mother, she was the gentlest dog Tom had ever known. She had been a present from his parents for his fifteenth birthday and they had been the best of friends for over fifteen years. She'd died six months ago and Tom had taken her death very hard. Tessa had been Tom's girlfriend for two years, not a natural dog lover, but she had tolerated Betty because she knew how much he loved his old dog. Secretly she had been hoping the mangy old mutt would die and they could get on with getting a cat, but then she had gone and had puppies and Tom couldn't bear to let the little black one go. The other three had gone to good homes but Tom had insisted on keeping Basil. Months of puppy training followed but Betty's health had sadly deteriorated and then she had died. All this had been too much for Tessa. She had upped and left.

Single now for nearly six months, Tom was happy enough. Unfortunately while Betty had been sweet-natured and gentle, Basil was like a black missile and had been virtually impossible to train – hence their early exit from Miss Graham's Dog Obedience and Socialisation classes.

After an hour's searching, Tom still hadn't seen any sign of Basil and needed to go home to have a shower as he was due in work. Tom worked as a reservations manager of a hotel, and he had half an hour to get there or Pierre, the general manager, and general pain-in-the-arse, would give him grief. Pierre had a nasty habit of spraying spit at who ever he was disciplining. He ate a lot of garlic so avoiding him was a top priority for all the staff at The Sullivan Hotel. Tom's eyes frantically roamed the pavements and front gardens of the houses as he made his way home, but to no avail.

At work Tom sat at his desk making "Missing" posters to stick on lampposts on his way home.

"Whatchya up to Tom?" asked Siobhan, one of the front desk girls, as she passed him hunched over his computer.

"Basil has gone missing," he said miserably

"Oh I'm so sorry. Have you tried the dog warden?" she asked as she lifted a pile of envelopes from the cabinet behind him.

"Dog warden? I hadn't thought of that." Tom added a nice blue background to Basil's poster.

"Just a suggestion. I hope he turns up." She patted his shoulder as she headed back out to the reception desk.

"Dog warden! That's brilliant, why didn't I think of that?" he muttered as he thumbed through the phone book looking for the council's number. The council, it turned out, had a full page of numbers. He found the number for Dog Control under Enforcement Officers, and dialled the number.

The phone rang four times and then a recorded message kicked in.

"Office hours are between 9:00am and 5:00pm, Monday to Friday," the voice message told him.

"Damn." He glanced at his watch. It was 7:00 pm. The dog wardens were long gone. He'd have to wait until the next morning.

The following morning he was on the phone first thing.

"A black Cocker Spaniel you say?" A gruff man on the other end of the phone went off to check if Basil had indeed been picked up the previous day.

"Aye, we have him, noisy wee blighter. Can you come and pick him up?"

"Absolutely, I'm on my way."

"There's a five pound fine by the way."

"I'll be there in twenty minutes."

Fifteen minutes later Tom pulled up at the dog warden's office. He could hear the barking of various dogs as he pulled open the door. The same gruff man he had spoken to on the phone, was sitting at the desk reading an auto magazine.

"Black Cocker Spaniel?"

Tom nodded.

"Hang on, I'll go and get him. Have a seat. It will take a couple of minutes. The guys are dealing with another dog at the minute."

Tom sat down on one of the plastic seats, and glanced around. The only other person in the waiting room was a very attractive blonde woman. She looked vaguely familiar. She smiled.

"Do they have your dog?"

"Yes thank goodness, I thought I'd lost him. He just took off yesterday," Tom grinned.

"Miss Graham's dog training classes?"

"Pardon?" Tom was puzzled.

"Your dog was sick in Miss Graham's dog training classes wasn't he?"

"Oh God yes he was. We didn't have much success," Tom laughed. He remembered her now. Still no wedding ring, he noticed.

"You had the Newfoundland pup?"

She nodded.

"Abigail Turner, I also failed the class." She giggled as she shook Tom's hand.

"You did?" Tom asked unable to take his eyes off her sparkly green ones.

"The week after you left Albie flattened two of the miniature Schnauzers and Miss Graham thought it best that we didn't come back."

"Well now I don't feel quite so bad."

"I was sorry you didn't come back to the class though," she smiled.

"You were?"

She blushed slightly. "I thought you were quite cute."

"You did?" Tom was rendered virtually speechless.

Suddenly there was a crash and a bang and the door behind the desk was flung open. The gruff man was hauled through the door by an enormous black bear-like dog who launched his huge frame on top of Abigail. Close behind was Basil, looking none the worse for his night in doggie prison. He bustled out, his tail still wagging in double time.

"Looks like these two are already friends," Abigail said as she finally managed to extract herself from a rapturous Albie.

"It certainly does," Tom replied giving Basil's velvety ears a rub.

"So, do you fancy taking these two for a walk?" Abigail asked as she put on Albie's lead.

"Basil you are a very good boy." Tom patted his dog's shiny black coat as they followed Abigail and Albie out of the dark office and strolled out into the sunny Wednesday morning.

Judi Curtin's books include *Sorry Walter,
From Claire to Here* and *Almost Perfect.*
Her children's books include *Alice
Next Door* and *Alice Again.*

31. STICKY'S BROTHER
Judi Curtin

They say that big boys don't cry, but Callum is only a little boy, and he was crying. In fact he was sobbing his little heart out. In between sniffles and sobs he managed to tell me that his class was making a big book, and every child had to write a story about his pet. His politically correct teacher said a friend's pet would do if you didn't have one of your own, but that wasn't good enough for Callum.

"I want to write about my own pet," he said. "I need a pet. Everyone else has a pet."

I seriously doubted that – maybe the other children in his class were better liars than he was. Then he played his trump card. "And I'm sad because I miss my daddy."

He only missed his daddy because he remembered nothing at all about him. Alex, Callum's dad, had packed his bag and left us three years ago. I cried as he loaded his bag into the back of his clapped-out Ford Capri, but it only took me days to realise that Alex was a feckless lazy waster, and that Callum and I had probably had a lucky escape.

I knew what Callum meant though – he missed the idea of a father in his life, just like I missed the idea of a man in mine. But Callum wasn't exactly a man-magnet and the men I encountered never wanted a woman with baggage – not even very cute baggage!

Anyway, as I dropped Callum to school that day, I promised we'd figure out the pet problem. It wouldn't be easy. I'd spent ages finding our house, and it was too soon to antagonize my new landlord by blatantly flouting his 'NO PETS' rule. It was going to have to be a very small, very quiet pet.

It took me about two hours. I scrabbled in the garden until I found a nice smooth oval-shaped stone. I washed and dried it, and painted it a nice shade of pinky-brown. I then added eyes, and a cute pink mouth. I cut a fringe from my new, very expensive suede boots, and made a tail. Then I made the ultimate sacrifice – I cut a lock of my own hair, and super-glued it to the creature's back. It looked like a crazed Mohican, but I was sure it would do the trick. I was wrong.

Callum looked at it, and then he looked at me.

I smiled brightly. "It's Rocky. Your new pet."

He looked at it for a while. Then he looked at me again. Surely his eyes were too young for such disdain. "It's a stone."

I smiled even more brightly. "No it's not. It's a pet rock."

"The big boys will laugh at me."

He was only in senior infants. How big could the big boys be? It didn't matter. The tears started again. It was back to the drawing board.

While Callum was at school the next day, I ran to the local pet shop. Behind the counter was a dangerous looking youth reading a soft-porn magazine. He raised one blood-shot eye.

"Want something?"

No. I just came in to enjoy your wonderful personality, and the smell of stale cat food.

I bit my tongue. "Actually, I want a very small, very quiet pet."

He inclined his head towards a large cage of furry things. "Hamster?"

I shook my head.

"Gerbil?"

I shook my head.

"Guinea pig?"

Couldn't he see that he was on the wrong track?

"White rat?"

This time I couldn't hide my shudder.

"Have you anything a bit less furry? A fish maybe?"

He shook his head. "Nope. All out of fish. Might have some next week."

Next week would be too late. What kind of a pet shop didn't have fish? I checked my watch. It was too late to go to town to try another shop.

I spoke again hopefully. "Anything else?"

The youth got up, and walked toward a plastic tank. It looked to be full of leaves and sticks.

"Stick insects," he said, treating me to the strong alcohol-scented whiff of his breath.

It cost seven euro, including a tank and seven free ivy leaves. Still, that wasn't a lot to pay for my baby's happiness.

When Callum got home, he looked at his new pet.

"I suppose it'll do." Not quite the enthusiastic response I had hoped for.

The story took almost an hour:

I have a stick insect. Its name is Sticky. It eats ivy leaves. I love Sticky.

As a story it didn't seem to quite capture the anguish that had preceded Sticky's arrival in our lives. And the last line was a blatant lie. Clearly, once the story was written, Callum didn't care if Sticky lived or died.

This turned out to be fortuitous, as Sticky died that night. Though not known for his activity, even I noticed that he hadn't moved in hours. I tapped the side of the tank, and Sticky tumbled over and lay on his back with his little stick-legs in the air.

Callum perked up when he heard the news. "Now we can have a funeral."

Sticky was duly placed in an empty butter carton, and buried in the garden, right next to the oil tank. His grave was adorned with daisies and dandelions. Many prayers were said.

Callum was happy when I dropped him to school.

He was crying when I collected him. "I forgot. I need a photo of my pet."

Time for more bright smiles. "Let's draw a nice picture instead."

He shook his head.

"We'll get a picture on the Internet. And we can print it onto real photo paper."

Even such extravagance wasn't enough for Callum.

"It has to be a real photo, and I have to take it myself."

I sighed. There was only one thing to do. When I accidentally signed up for motherhood, I had a vague idea I was taking on too much. I never thought it would lead to grave-robbing.

Sticky was duly disinterred, and replaced in his tank. I had managed to get most of the butter off his head, and he didn't look too bad, propped up against a pile of ivy. Not good enough for Callum.

"But he's dead."

I shook my head. "Maybe I made a mistake. I think I saw his leg move."

There were more tears and the journey to school next day wasn't a happy one. Callum sobbed all the way. "I need the photo tomorrow, or all the big boys will laugh at me."

"Don't worry," I smiled. "Mummy will think of something." I wondered if the big boys were open to bribes or threats.

After work I legged it back to the pet-shop. The same youth was there, reading the same magazine. "Want something?"

I felt a strong urge to drag him over the counter and punch his greasy face. I resisted. I didn't want him setting the hamsters on me.

"I'd like another stick insect please."

"No can do."

How could that be? He'd had loads, and there was hardly a sudden rush on them.

"They're all gone. Passed away. They've gone to a better place."

Well, that wouldn't have been hard.

The boy was suddenly almost chatty. "Must've been a virus. I could give you a dead one, if you like."

Actually, I had one of those already.

"But please. It's an emergency. I have to have a stick insect by tomorrow."

Was I pleading with this slimy waste-of-space?

To my surprise, he actually put down his magazine, and honoured me with a look at both red-rimmed eyes at once. "There's a guy on Jasper Road who has lots."

Jasper Road? That was my road?

"What number?"

Greasy-boy shrugged. "Dunno. He's got a red car."

Jasper Road was very long, and there were seven red cars. I was on the fifth "excuse me, but do you happen to keep stick insects?" before I got a response other than laughter, or threats to call the guards.

A wry-looking man with nice blue eyes leaned on his doorway. "Actually, I do keep stick insects. Why do you want to know?"

I babbled out my story, wishing I'd put on something other than my oldest track-suit. He looked upset. "The poor little guy. I love kiddies. I hate to see them sad."

Had I heard right? He loved kiddies? Was it too soon to propose marriage? He brought me in, and I surveyed the room for signs of female occupation. There were none. I selected an insect similar to Sticky – well it was brown and about the right size. Blue-eyes put him into a jar for me. As I went down the drive, he called me back. "There's just one thing."

I turned back. There always was one more thing, wasn't there?

He grinned at me. "I'd like to retain visiting rights."

"I think that could be arranged."

Callum eyed the creature for a long time.

My bright smile returned. "Look, love. Isn't it wonderful? Sticky's back."

"It's not Sticky. Is it?"

Part of being a mother is knowing when to stop lying.

I shook my head. "No, darling, it's not Sticky."

I thought I could see the beginnings of a tear. I couldn't take more tears.

"Actually, it's Sticky's brother."

Another important part of being a mother is deciding when it's appropriate to start lying again.

Callum folded his arms. "I suppose he'll do."

Sticky's brother was photographed from many angles, before the young photographer was happy. A photograph was duly selected, and printed, and carefully placed within the pages of Callum's homework diary.

Next morning Callum skipped along the road beside me. Blue-eyes was coming out of his house. I stopped and smiled. I owed this man big-time. He smiled too. "About those visiting rights," he said, "how about I drop over tomorrow?"

It wouldn't be fair to come between a man and his pet. "It's number fifteen," I said. "Any time after six is fine."

Callum and I walked on. "Who's he?" he asked.

"He's Sticky's brother's dad. He's going to come and visit him."

Callum shrugged. "OK."

We walked on some more.

"You know, Mum," Callum said. "I think I love Sticky's brother more than I loved Sticky. Sticky was a bit boring."

I smiled to myself. Sticky's brother was hardly a barrel of laughs, but he'd already brought more happiness to my small family than his little stick-brain could ever comprehend.

Mary Bond's books include
Absolutely Love and *All Things Perfect*.

www.mary-bond.com

32. CALL HIM BARNEY
Mary Bond

"I think you should get a dog."

"A dog? Are you mad?" I stared at my sister as though she had two heads.

"On the contrary, Gemma, I think it would be the best thing possible."

"Don't be ridiculous," I snapped. I turned to stare out the window at my son. Outside in the back garden, six-year-old Jamie was half-heartedly kicking a football around on the grass. I looked at his lone figure in the football jersey that was two sizes too big and I felt my heart contract.

It was a beautiful afternoon at the start of summer, the kind of day that held the promise of long, sultry evenings dissolving into warm, velvety nights. The kind of day that made you feel either terribly happy or sad, depending on what was going on in your life. Sunshine licked the soft leaves blossoming on the silver birch tree and blazed across the overgrown riot of pansies crammed into planters along the patio. They looked likes rows of smiley faces as they waved and bobbed in the gentle breeze. I didn't feel like smiling back. I couldn't even remember having planted them, but obviously I had.

Before.

Abruptly I turned back to face my sister. I caught her off guard, because I saw the raw pity in her eyes before she hurriedly rearranged her features into the semblance of a smile.

She lifted up the bottle of sauvignon blanc. "More?"

"Yeah, sure, why not," I said as I pushed forward my glass. It was early in the evening and we had almost finished the bottle. So what. There was plenty more where it came from. I watched as Fiona topped up my glass, and the pale gold liquid swirled around. I anticipated its chilled taste on my lips and the dull fog that would wrap around the edge of my thoughts and mask the hurt for a little while longer.

"Getting back to the dog . . ." Fiona began.

"No way."

"Believe me, it would work wonders. Really, Gemma."

"And what makes you the expert?"

Fiona tried another tack. "You were talking about getting one before, weren't you? You and Tom . . . ?" Then she suddenly realised that she was straying into forbidden territory. "Before" territory.

"I'm just trying to help," she shrugged, looking clumsy and embarrassed.

"I know that," I said, reaching across to touch her hand to assuage her discomfort. It was something new I'd had to get used to dealing with, along with everything else. Other people's discomfort. It was amazing how awkward it made me feel, considering everything I'd been through. Some fancy psychoanalyst would probably say it was a form of self-imposed guilt. But since I wasn't into psychoanalysts or therapy, any type of self-examination was a no-go area. I didn't really care.

"I really think it would do the trick you know . . . it's a

well known fact that having a dog cures a whole host of ills. You should seriously consider it."

"You've forgotten something absolutely critical," I told her.

"What's that?"

In spite of everything, I felt a sudden urge to laugh. I could see by Fiona's solemn face that she was casting her mind around, wondering what grave, momentous oversight she could have made.

"Just one little factor," I said. "I happen to be afraid of dogs."

"Is that all? Afraid of a little dog? Now you're being ridiculous," she accused me.

"Maybe so, but it's very real to me. And they're not all that little. Some of them are quite big, you know, all teeth and snarly mouth."

She shook her head. "I never heard such rubbish."

"Well, I'm sorry, but it's just not on. You've no idea how petrified I feel when I have to pass one on the street. I wouldn't even go for a walk in the park by myself in case they're jumping around unleashed."

"Unleashed? You make it sound like you're talking about a wild animal."

"That's exactly how it feels to me. Even thinking about it now brings me out in a cold sweat. It makes my heart beat faster and turns my legs to jelly."

I couldn't believe I was having this conversation. A normal conversation, where I wasn't furiously thinking in advance of everything I was about to utter. For once my attention was focussed on something other than Before.

Fiona sat back and looked at me thoughtfully.

"Okay. I take your point. There are ways around it, you

know. You could easily be cured. Sorry . . . bad choice of words . . ." She shook her head apologetically.

I took a gulp of wine and waited for the moment to pass.

My sister also took a gulp of wine and after a while she continued. "You could learn you know, to get rid of your phobia, there are ways and means . . ."

Just then Jamie wandered into the kitchen, football in hand. His blonde hair was slightly tousled but his oversized jersey was far too clean and once more my heart contracted.

"I'll think about it," I told Fiona.

A week later, we were walking in the park. It was a sunny evening and green swathes of parkland were dotted with children and parents, lovers and friends. And dogs. Millions of dogs.

"Now stay calm. Take a deep breath and count to ten," Fiona said. "See that little Terrier ahead, safely on its owner's lead? We're going to stroll as near to it as you can, just as though we're going for a walk. And when you feel it's too close for comfort, we'll back off. Isn't he a cute little dog? Really nice and friendly," she soothed, as we walked towards the little animal with my hand clutching her arm. "Nothing for you to worry about."

I got within ten feet before breaking into a sweat.

"Good. Very good," Fiona said encouragingly. "We'll walk on a bit further and try another dog. Maybe next time you'll get a little closer before you panic."

"So long as people don't think I'm some kind of dog pervert," I muttered grimly, catching the curious glance of the Terrier's owner.

"Don't worry about them. I see just the dog ahead, a lovely Labrador. C'mon."

This was Fiona's idea, her brainchild. When I told her

that I'd decided to get rid of my phobia, she immediately went shopping. She snapped up an armful of self-help books on the subject in order to put together a personalised programme. First on her action plan was to get me used to being in the general vicinity of a dog. The local park beckoned.

I managed to get within six feet of the Labrador before I chickened out. But our third attempt, some kind of Cocker Spaniel, almost caused me to be attacked. Not by the dog, mind you, but by the owner. Fiona's plan was to go no nearer than six feet, but to remain at that radius for at least ten minutes. Not so easy when the dog kept stopping to snuffle in the undergrowth and dart in and out of the grassy bank alongside the path. After a few minutes, the pensioner owner looked as though she was about to batter me with her walking stick. We backed away, laughing and tittering. I couldn't remember the last time I had laughed so carelessly. Maybe there was something to be said for this dog lark after all.

"Now rub your hand along the fur, feel how velvety it is to the touch . . . soft and silky. That's right. Good. Caress it gently and stroke it in one direction only."

I gingerly followed Fiona's instructions and duly petted and stroked.

"That's it," she continued in a soothing voice. "Keep it up . . . slow, gentle movements. I think you're getting the hang of it, Gemma. Well done . . . Now close your eyes and pretend it's a dog."

I closed my eyes for a split second, but then almost immediately jumped to my feet. Fiona's faux fur collar, detached with due care from her winter jacket and wrapped around a kitchen roll tube, dropped to the ground.

"What's the matter? You were doing great."

"Yeah, until I visualised a real live dog."

"You had the movement right anyway," she said, a glint in her eye. "Next step is the real thing."

"No way. I'm a long way from buying a dog, no matter how small and tame it is."

"Who said anything about buying one?"

I frowned. "Surely that's the point of all this?" Apart from any agenda, however, I had to admit I was quite enjoying my "therapy" sessions with my sister. It took me out of myself, away to a different place, where Before didn't exist.

"Didn't I tell you?" Fiona grinned. "We're going to borrow a dog."

"Borrow one?"

"Yeah, Sadie next door has a gorgeous Jack Russell she's dying for you to meet."

"Oh my God."

I'm not sure if Fiona's tactics were strictly legitimate. Or if she really devoured all those self-help books in order to apply the correct principles. All I know is that some four weeks after our talk in the kitchen, we were driving down to a Tipperary kennel with Jamie strapped into the back seat, en route to fetch a dog, a puppy, or for all I knew, perhaps my nemesis.

I drove down and Fiona drove back. She planned it like this, so that all the way home, I could sit with the dog on my lap and bond with it, so to speak.

He was the smallest of a litter of five and he slept most of the way. Curled up on my lap, he was a warm ball of fur. I waited for flutters of anxiety in my stomach, a quickening heartbeat and beads of sweat, and I breathed slowly and calmly. Then I became aware of the comforting heat of the puppy on my lap and a pleasant warmth seeping through my body. It seemed a long time since I had experienced such warmth. I reached out tentative hands and gently stroked his short white fur. The puppy snuggled in even closer and I felt a ridiculous sense of achievement.

"Mum?" This was Jamie, from the back seat, awake and drowsy after his nap.

"Yes, love?"

"Can we call him Barney?"

"Barney?" It wasn't hard to guess where Jamie had heard that. But it didn't matter. The important thing was that he was involved. "That's a great name, love."

We were hitting the outskirts of the city centre before he spoke again. "Will Barney be afraid?"

"Why should he be afraid, darling?"

"He might be scared of his new home."

"He won't be scared with us to take care of him."

"Yes, but . . ." and then added in a rush, "will he not miss his mummy and daddy? Or his brothers and sisters?"

"Yes, darling, he probably will, in the beginning," I said, my voice calm. "But he'll have us to love, won't he?"

"I s'pose."

"And you can talk to him about his family so he won't forget them."

"And Mum . . . can I talk to him 'bout Cian?"

"Yes, love."

I sensed rather than saw the sheen of tears in Fiona's eyes. Gruffly I told her to concentrate on the road.

By the time Tom came home that evening, Jamie was already in bed.

"What the hell is that?" He pointed to Barney, fast asleep in his dog basket in the kitchen.

"What does it look like?"

"A bloody dog."

"It's not a bloody dog. His name is Barney. I got him for Jamie."

"What the hell did you go and do that for?"

"I thought it would be good for Jamie to have a puppy."

"And did it not cross your mind to talk to me first?"

"Yes, but you might have said no."

"Too right." He opened the newspaper signalling the end of the conversation and my stomach heaved. It had been a mistake. A great blooming, ghastly mistake. So much for Fiona's brilliant idea.

I didn't think that dogs could cry, but on his first night, the whimpering noises coming from Barney could only be described as crying. My son crept back downstairs in his pyjamas and I watched as he stroked the puppy and talked to him. I told Jamie it was perfectly okay for puppies and, indeed, people to cry. Tom remained silent behind the wall of his newspaper.

Over the next few days I mopped up more spills than I ever thought possible from Barney. I told Jamie that it was a perfectly normal thing to happen. We started to bring him out for walks, Jamie and I, but Tom refused to come. We went to the park and ran around with Barney and as days slipped into weeks, Jamie looked lively and alert in a way he hadn't looked for ages. He started to sleep better and stopped wetting the bed.

"Thought you were afraid of dogs," Tom said to me brusquely one evening.

"Yeah, I am. This is only a trial run," I told him.

When Barney was with us for three weeks, he tore the newspaper to shreds just before Tom had a chance to bury himself behind it and I waited for the sky to fall in. It didn't. Then one evening I caught Tom watching the telly with Barney on his lap, and I fled into the kitchen and stuffed my hand into my mouth.

And at last, one Sunday afternoon, Tom said yes when Jamie asked him to come to the park with us. At first he walked stiffly and he looked as though he'd rather be anywhere else. He began to thaw out when Jamie showed him the tricks he'd taught Barney. He actually sat down on the grass and began to play with the puppy. Jamie, chortling with delight, threw himself on his dad as though he was a long lost friend. I watched in amazement as my son, my husband and Barney rolled around together on the grass. Jamie asked his dad if he would start playing football with him again 'cos it was no fun without him or Cian, and Tom ruffled his hair and said yes.

Then Jamie was up and away, running with Barney, showing how fast they could race. Tom grabbed my hand and urged me along. It was the first time in months he touched me like this and my heart sang as we chased Jamie and Barney across the grass. I was afraid to look into his eyes when we eventually stopped, completely out of breath. I felt what I thought was his kiss on my forehead, but I was still afraid to look.

We all landed home, a raggle taggle group, tired and exhausted. Jamie fell asleep on Tom's lap and my husband carefully and tenderly carried him up to bed. And just as carefully and tenderly, he turned to me that night and my heart lifted as I went into his arms. Tom, who had locked himself away when our elder son became ill and died, had finally returned to us.

Melissa Hill's books include *Something You Should Know, Not What You Think, The Last to Know, Wishful Thinking, Never Say Never* and *All Because Of You.*

www.melissahill.info

33. RIVALS
Melissa Hill

It all started when six-year-old Jamie started talking about getting a dog.

"Mum, I asked Dad if we could get a puppy, and he said to ask you . . . can we Mum, can we please?"

"Hmm, did he now?"

Lucy couldn't stand dogs, couldn't stand their pathetic drooling and panting, hated the way they were so submissive and needy and . . . dirty. No, she thought, cats were a much better choice of pet. Cats were proud, graceful, independent, clean and tidy and they wouldn't dream of digging up the back garden just because the notion struck them!

Any talk of bringing a dog into this house was bound to cause problems. She should have known, really. There was never a mention about getting a dog when they lived in the city centre – in that shoebox apartment. But once the family moved into their new house in the suburbs, Lucy supposed it was inevitable that the subject would rear its ugly head. Here, there was plenty of room for a scabby mutt to run wild and cause havoc, as the silly creatures were apt to do.

"Can we Mum, please?" Jamie asked again, his brown eyes wide and beseeching as he stared up at his mother.

"Maybe . . . we'll see," she replied vaguely, just as her husband entered the kitchen.

"I thought we might take a trip down to the animal refuge on Saturday and take a look – what do you think? " Chris suggested, causing Jamie to grin with pleasure while Lucy bristled with disdain.

The animal refuge? Ugh! Who knew what kind of diseases they'd pick up in a place like that?

"I don't know – maybe we should think some more about this first," she said. "A dog is a big commitment and needs lots of looking after, whereas cats are a lot less hassle."

"But I want a dog!" Jamie wailed and Lucy felt like throttling him.

"Honey, we promised Jamie we'd think about it when we moved here," Chris said sitting down alongside his wife and putting an arm around her, evidently hoping to soften her up. "You know I've always wanted one. We always had dogs at home when I was growing up, and it was great. I also think it would be good for Jamie – help teach him some responsibility."

"But it's a huge responsibility Chris, and not just for Jamie. Dogs need so much looking after. They need feeding and lots of walking."

"I'll look after that side of it," her husband interjected. "I'll make sure he's walked and fed."

"Yay!" Hearing this, Jamie leapt gleefully into the air, and with a heavy heart, Lucy realised that the decision had already been made. They were getting a bloody dog – whether she liked it or not.

The following Saturday morning, Chris and Jamie paid a visit to the local ISPCA centre. Lucy decided not to go along with them; those kind of places made her uncomfortable. No, better just to let them off themselves and get it over with. Anyway, with any luck there might not even be a cute puppy at the centre. Those places were probably packed to the gills with older abandoned mutts who had outstayed their welcomes elsewhere. Funny how that rarely seemed to happen with cats, Lucy thought. Dogs got shunted out of houses by the shed-load, whereas cats just tended to do their own thing and pretty much stayed out of their owner's way. Really, cats were a much more superior pet, but in their present mood, Lucy knew it would be impossible to convince Jamie and Chris of the fact.

They were back within the hour, and by Jamie's elated expression from the backseat as the car pulled into the driveway, Lucy knew the trip had been a success. She was slightly irked that they had found a suitable animal first time round, having hoped it might take a little longer. She'd been planning on convincing the two men in her life to abandon the idea altogether. And speaking of being abandoned . . .

The scrawny, bedraggled creature that stepped tentatively out of the backseat of the car looked so pitiful that for a second Lucy thought it was all a big joke. The state of it! Long scraggy hair, mournful eyes and thin shivering body . . . for Heaven's sake what was the attraction? It was some class of Red Setter, those dopey-looking dogs they used on the TV ads for the bus company, although she knew it was about as far from pure-bred as a dog could get. And the stink! Even from this distance, Lucy could smell Eau de Refuge.

"Hey Mum, say hello to Rio!" Jamie enthused, putting his arms around the silly mutt, who just stood there looking petrified. Rio? What kind of a name was that? Lucy supposed it had something to do with that idiotic football team he and Chris followed, something United. Hmm, perhaps the name was fitting for the silly mongrel after all.

"I think Rio needs a good scrubbing," she replied, glancing meaningfully at her husband, who was standing with his elbow on the car door, and grinning from ear to ear.

"Let's just give him an hour or two to get used to the place, then we'll get him cleaned up," Chris replied easily.

An hour or two? Lucy sincerely hoped they weren't thinking of letting the stinking so-and-so into her house smelling like that!

But thankfully Jamie led Rio through the side gate and out into the back garden, whereby the dog proceeded to christen each and every flowerbed in sight. Lucy winced as she watched him.

After a few hours, and greatly aided by Chris and Jamie's gentle coaxing, the dog seemed to overcome his initial nervousness, and gradually began to come out of himself. He even broached a tentative sniff at Lucy while the others watched with interest, obviously willing her to accept the new addition to the family. But Lucy remained unmoved. She just wasn't a dog lover and never would be. Yes, she'd put up with it; for the family's sake she'd have to, but from now on Lucy would be watching, and if that dirty mutt put one paw out of step, she'd make sure he was out on his floppy red ear.

Two weeks later, the family was relaxing in the back garden, all of them soaking up the unusually warm Sunday afternoon sunshine, while a considerably more animated Rio lay panting in the shade. Ugh, didn't he realise how undignified that looked? Lucy wondered, as she stretched out languorously in the sun. Why couldn't he keep his messy drooling and long pink tongue to himself?

Having spent the last fortnight in his company, Lucy was now fully convinced that the dog hadn't half a brain in his head. This was no great revelation, and indeed was something she'd always suspected, but given that this was her first time in close proximity to any dog, she was quite amazed at how correct her earlier assessment had been. But strangely, the mutt's inherent dimness only served to make the others adore him even more.

"Ah, look at Rio, isn't he so cute?" Jamie said lovingly when one morning he spied the dog on his back on the grass, paws in the air, rolling around and groaning like a half-wit. Jamie and Chris were nearly in tears laughing out the window at him.

Cute? He thought that was cute? Well, Lucy decided, determinedly ignoring the dog's idiotic behaviour, each to his own.

Today, Jamie had some friends over, each as energetic and boisterous as himself. Chris had installed one of those inflatable swimming pools on the lawn and with the midday temperatures hitting the twenties, the boys were making great use of it, splashing in and out of it and screaming at the top of their lungs.

Rio, typically gormless, seemed to think the pool was one huge drinking bowl and continued to slurp repeatedly out of one side. The boys were of course, delighted with this, and Rio in turn appeared to revel in their enthusiasm and the attention they were paying him. He seemed particularly excitable today, Lucy thought, watching the dog race after a football one of the boys had thrown for him to fetch.

"They seem to be enjoying themselves," Chris, commented, as he stretched out on a towel alongside his wife. "Rio included."

She smiled indulgently. "Go on then, say it."

"Say what?"

"What you've been dying to say for the last few weeks. 'I told you so'."

She rubbed sunscreen onto her shoulders. "I was very against it at the beginning, but I must admit he hasn't been too much trouble, and Jamie obviously adores him."

Lucy then grimaced. Now they'd be stuck with the blasted dog forever! She groaned. The heat must be getting to her.

Chris began to nuzzle her neck. "Well, I never thought I'd see the day."

"See what day?" she asked smiling coyly and leaning back onto his chest.

"The day my cat-mad wife would be won over by an uncivilised mutt."

"I haven't been won over," she countered, but the response was decidedly half-hearted. "I still prefer cats."

Chris kissed her softly on the lips. "Thank you for letting us have him – you're the best."

Soon, their kisses became more passionate, and after a quick check that the boys were okay, she and Chris got up and made to move back inside the house for some privacy. Their backs were barely turned, when one of Jamie's play-mates, Gordon decided to get up to mischief. Lucy had always suspected that the kid had a bit of a mean streak in him, but even she couldn't have anticipated what he was about to do next.

"Hey watch this!" Gordon yelled, grinning wickedly as he ran from one end of the garden to the other. The other boys stopped playing with the football and turned to look at him, Rio bounding around eagerly at their feet.

As she suddenly realised what was about to happen, Lucy's

eyes widened and her heart hammered in her chest. An icy fear raced along her spine, and for a split second, she almost forgot to breathe. He wouldn't, would he? Oh God, he would!

After that, it seemed like everything was happening in slow motion. Gordon raced forward, and Lucy knew she couldn't stop him. Then all of a sudden . . .

"Gordon NO!" Jamie roared, racing towards the pool to save his friend, who was now thrashing around in the water and evidently in great distress.

"What?" Gordon sneered. "It's only a stupid –"

Lucy felt as though her mind was about to explode. White noise buzzed in her ears yet through the din she thought she could hear voices . . . cries . . . shouts. Then, out of nowhere, she thought she heard a dog growl, then a snarl and then . . . then mercifully it was all over.

"Ahh, the dog's attacking me!" Gordon yelled, moving quickly away from the pool. Lucy breathed a huge sigh of relief. It was all over. It was OK. Eventually, her heart began to slow as she realised that there was no more danger. Everything was OK.

And yes, sure enough, there was Rio snarling and pulling out of the little brat's leg. Well, well, well . . . maybe she'd misjudged him after all.

Now Jamie was shouting at Gordon. "Why did you have to go and do that for? That's a horrible thing to do!"

Gordon tried to disentangle himself from Rio. "It was no big deal! I just wanted to see what would happen! What did your stupid dog have to go and attack me for?" he said, his lower lip quivering. He looked considerably less brave now.

"Because you were doing something horrible – that's why!"

Evidently sensing his job was done, Rio finally let go of Gordon's jeans and settled himself protectively in front of the pool. In the meantime, Lucy had come out of her fearful daze and had finally managed to move.

"What's going on here?" Chris asked, as he approached the pool. "What was all the shouting about?"

He looked from Jamie to Gordon to the other boys and once again to his son. "Jamie?"

"Gordon tried to drown her, but Rio saved her!" Jamie informed his father.

"I didn't want to drown him!" Gordon blubbered. "Honestly I didn't – I just wanted to see what he'd do!"

"It's not a he – it's a she!" Jamie corrected him.

Jamie's mother put her hands on her hips. "I think it's time you boys went home," she said sternly. "Gordon, I bet if your mum and dad knew about this, they'd be very, very disappointed in you."

"Please don't tell them Mrs Kelly, I'm really sorry Mrs Kelly," he sniffled as Jamie's mum led him and the others out front.

"Rio saved her?" Chris queried his son, looking mildly impressed.

Jamie nodded in assent. "Gordon wouldn't listen to me, so Rio kept pulling at his trousers until he let her go. I think he knew Dad!"

"Knew what?"

"I think he knew . . . you know . . . that she was afraid of water, that cats were afraid of water."

"Maybe he did," Chris agreed squatting down, and giving the wet and bedraggled (but considerably less agitated) family cat a gentle rub. Feeling much better after her horrible ideal, Lucy managed an appreciate purr.

"Do you think they might be friends now Dad?" Jamie asked.

"Who?"

"Rio and Lucy of course."

"I don't know Jamie. Cats and dogs aren't usually friends – and Lucy hasn't really taken to Rio since he moved in."

Lucy stood up on all fours and arched her bag against Jamie's legs. She gave a surreptitious glance at the gormless mutt, who was lying some distance away, tongue out and tail wagging, and she thought, still looking as idiotic as ever.

He had saved her life today however – had actually saved her from drowning. Was it a coincidence, or did he really know that her kind were afraid of water?

From day one Lucy had seen Rio as a rival, as a threat to her cosy position as resident pet in this family. From day one she'd believed dogs to be a greatly inferior species; unenlightened, unintelligent dimwits. But maybe, Lucy decided grudgingly, just maybe she'd been wrong.

Rio stared back at his supposed superior, his tongue out, his expression blank as ever. But then, as the two pets followed the others back inside the house, Lucy could have sworn that Rio had given her a knowing wink.

Andrea Semple's books include
The Ex-factor, *The Make-up Girl* and
The Man from Perfect.

www.andreasemple.com

34. A CAT OWNER'S GUIDE TO SEDUCTION

Andrea Semple

He was gorgeous. Really, truly beautiful. When I saw those sparkling, green I-know-what-you're-thinking eyes, my heart melted. It really did. There was no way I was going to leave such a dark, gorgeous stranger on the doorstep.

I had never seen anyone quite like Lord Byron. Before I met him, my life had seemed strangely incomplete. Now that he is here by my side, the long winter evenings seem so much more bearable. And all he demands from me is a warm lap, a regular bowl of milk and a daily tin of Chicken and Turkey Whiskas. Or, so I thought.

After eleven months of devoted TLC, it turns out that the stray cat who snuck his way into my home – not to mention my heart – demands a lot more from me. In short, the feline aristocrat wants me all to himself. If another male, especially those of the human variety, enters my flat, then he will do everything in his power to make sure said human never comes back.

The first time I realised this was the Pablo evening. Pablo was the Argentinean waiter who I invited back for a coffee, which spilt all over his leg when Lord Byron jumped up and headbutted the cup.

'Your cat eez crazy cat!' Pablo yelped as I padded his jeans with a cool damp cloth.

'Oh I'm sure it was only an accident. It was only an accident, wasn't it Byron?'

'And was scratching my face an accident too?'

Lord Byron was purring blissfully on the sofa, looking rather too proud of himself.

'He eez crazy!' Pablo kept on, close to tears from the scalding coffee. 'He has the devil inside of a-him! He eez Lucifer cat!'

At the time I thought Pablo was a nutcase, or was at least displaying an excess of Latin temperament, so I wasn't too upset when he left without even waiting for his wet patch to dry.

But pretty soon, Lord Byron was at it again, this time with Jeremy.

Ah yes, Jeremy. The lawyer. Quite dishy too, with the kind of eyes that seem to invite themselves under your duvet. Bit public school, with a Famous Five childhood, a year building Third World bridges somewhere behind him, and posh as a polo tournament. But a nice guy.

I'd gone on a few dates with him. Just drinks after work. I'd met him at some charity auction, which *Shine Communications* (the company I work for) had organised. He bid for a speedboat and a tie signed by a weatherman. He missed out on the boat, but got the tie, along with my number. He was a randy thing if I remember rightly, but I kept him at bay for three dates until I finally succumbed and invited him back to my place.

After the Pablo incident I was a bit worried about Lord Byron, but as he was nowhere to be seen, I quickly dragged Jeremy by his signed tie into the bedroom and shut the door behind us. Sixty seconds later we were in bed. Naked. Tantalisingly close to sex. And then, this happened:

'You seem, er . . . very hairy.'

'Hairy?' I asked him, ready to mention his freakishly small nipples and Dyson-patented kissing technique. 'Hairy?'

But before I had time to thump him, he lifted back the duvet.

'I think we have a visitor,' he said. And he was right. For there in the dark cave of the duvet lay Lord Byron, his purr on the mute setting for once, looking at us like a disapproving parent.

'Byron,' I said pulling back the duvet. 'You can lie on Mummy's bed all day tomorrow. But tonight you're going to have to make do with your basket.'

As I tried to lift Lord Byron off the bed he unsheathed his claws and clung onto the sheet.

'Come on,' I said, realising the heat of the moment was now about as hot as a wet lettuce, 'off you go.'

Jeremy looked at me and laughed as I tried to prise my cat off the new sheet. His laughter quickly died as one of Lord Byron's paws caught hold of something else.

'Aaagh! His claws! Aaagh! Get him off! He's . . . aagh! In my . . . Aagh!'

First round to Lord Byron.

But that was then.

That was before Lord Byron met his match. Before Jake Harper, the vet. The one who cured Lord Byron's conjunctivitis. The one who I bumped into at Sainsbury's – our trolleys colliding near the deli counter – before he stuttered his way around to asking me out on date.

'Yes!' I said, in a Charlie-Bucket-finding-Willy-Wonka's-one-remaining-golden-ticket kind of way.

I may have seemed a tad over-enthusiastic but this was absolutely perfect. Not only was Jake a 6 foot 1 package of hunkiness with the kind of sad, helpless eyes of a man who had seen too much animal pain, but he was also already familiar with Lord Byron's temperament.

When he'd come to give him his eye drops, my darling pet had turned into a hissing, hedgehog of a devil-cat, who would have probably scratched poor Jake's helpless eyes out of the sockets if I hadn't been pinning him to the table – Lord Byron, not Jake.

So anyway, Jake takes me for a drink. He pours out the wine, and his heart, and immediately we hit it off. Two weeks and four dates later, he was at my flat, meeting my cat on his own turf.

Needless to say, Lord Byron spent most of the time sitting on my knee and making sure Jake kept his hands to himself.

When Jake moved in for a stroke (of the cat, not me), Lord Byron opened his eyes and simultaneously swiped his claws deep into his wrist.

'Agh,' he said, tearing his arm away. 'That hurt.'

'He must be a bit jealous,' I said, trying to act surprised. 'He's used to having me all to himself.'

Lord Byron hissed, hatefully, kind of proving my point.

'Maybe he'll warm to you. In time.'

And maybe not. In fact, if anything, Lord Byron seemed more hostile to Jake than all the other poor unfortunate men who had previously crossed his path. It was all there in his body language: the way he walked straight past Jake, even when he spoke his name, blanking him out of existence. The most Jake could hope for was an arrogant tail-flick or a cold stare. Maybe he remembered the eye drops.

Lord Byron spent most of the evening testing Jake's

masculinity. After all, from the perspective of a muscular tom cat whose favourite past-time was killing birds and mice with his teeth, a vegetarian vet must have seemed quite feeble.

First there was the scratching. Then he moved from claws to teeth in a deliberate effort to highlight his low pain threshold.

'Onowowowowowowowow,' Jake said, as Lord Byron bit firmly into his little finger.

'Oh, he's only giving you a love-bite,' I told him. 'It means he likes you.'

'He's agh liking me a bit too often,' Jake said, blinking water out of his eyes.

'Come on, Lord B,' I said, placing my little finger between Jake's hand and my cat's flesh-hungry jaws. 'Jake doesn't want to play.'

I hoisted the aspiring lion away from Jake's hand and relegated him to the carpet. Trying to repair the situation, I then rested my head on Jake's chest, curled my legs up onto the settee and switched on the TV. It was so nice, feeling the warmth of a man, and the beat of his heart – such a change from the purr of a cat.

While we spent the evening watching house-hunting shows, Lord Byron spent the evening watching our blanket occupation of the sofa. The hatred in his eyes only grew as he lay there, staring, brooding, wishing Jake was a mouse, or a bird, or anything else he could really get his teeth into.

Then a small miracle happened. Lord Byron stood up and walked out of the living room, across the kitchen and through the cat-flap, leaving myself and Jake in peace.

'That has never happened before,' I told Jake.

'What hasn't?'

'The cat has never left me alone when I've had other, er, friends round.'

Jake seemed rather proud. 'Oh, so does this mean I've passed the test?'

'If you're good enough for Lord Byron, you're good enough for me.'

'Why did you call him Lord Byron?' Jake asked, perhaps a little embarrassed.

'I, er, don't know. I studied Lord Byron at university. And I think the name sort of suits him.'

'Mad, bad and dangerous to know?'

'Something like that.'

But as the evening went on it seemed Lord Byron's mad, bad and dangerous tendencies towards my house-guest were on the wane. But then I heard a suspicious noise from the kitchen and went to investigate.

'Won't be a mo,' I assured Jake.

When I got to the kitchen, I nearly fainted in horror. For right there, on the floor, there was some kind of creature. The feathers signified a bird, but a bird soaked in its own blood.

It was still, technically speaking alive, beating its one good wing as its black blinkless eyes bulged with panic. Sitting above the half-dead creature was Lord Byron, purring in quiet celebration of his achievement. Strands of feather stuck to his blood-glossed chest like war medals.

'Jake!' I screamed. 'Jake! I need you! Here! Now! Please! Quickly!'

Jake ran to the kitchen, with a face that looked ready to confront a burglar.

'What is it?' he asked, but then saw for himself. 'Right, he said, with the cool authority of a doctor on ER. 'Kitchen paper. Have you got any kitchen paper?'

I turned around, picked a roll up from the unit and handed it to him. 'There,' I said.

'OK,' Jake said, as he pressed paper over the bird's wound.

By this point, Lord Byron had sneaked away to the corner of the kitchen, and lay himself down by the bin.

'And some water,' Jake said. 'Could you get me some water?'

The requests kept coming. Paper. Water. A needle and thread. Vodka (a better antiseptic than Baileys apparently). Aspirin (Aspirin?). And there, right on my kitchen floor, he undid Lord Byron's vicious damage.

'There,' he said, after twenty minutes. 'She should be all right now.'

And picking up the blackbird in his hands, and holding it as if it was the most fragile thing in the world, said, 'Lily, could you open the door please?'

So I opened the back door and watched Jake walk out, crouch down and place the frightened creature on the unmown lawn.

I went outside and watched the bird twitch its head around, as if seeing the world for the first time, before spreading its wings. Tears itched behind my eyes, and I felt slightly overwhelmed. It was at that precise moment that Jake placed his arm around me and the bird flew off into the sky, fading into a dot, then dissolving into the night.

As Jake held me, I thought about the tiny miracle that had just occurred. A bird, on the edge of death, brought back to life in my kitchen with nothing more than some kitchen paper, a needle and thread, and the contents of the medicine box.

After another minute of silence, we headed back inside, Lord Byron watching us from his position by the bin.

'Naughty cat,' I tell him. 'Naughty, naughty cat.'

But I am not angry.

'He can't help it,' Jake said, softly. 'He's just a cat. Cats kill birds. That's what they do. It's their nature.'

But Lord Byron's nature seemed to have suddenly been transformed. He followed us into the living room and rubbed his head against Jake's leg, his purr happily motoring away.

'He must have changed his mind about me,' Jake said.

'Yes,' I said. 'He must.'

And as the three of us curled up on the sofa, I thought about another miracle. A miracle I thought would never happen to me. One that had taken place this evening, as I'd watched Jake's large steady hands save a fragile creature on my kitchen lino. The way I had felt as he placed his arm around me. I had felt so warm, despite the cold night air. And as we sat on the sofa, content in our silence, it was easy to imagine that Lord Byron's happy purr, was in fact my own. That I was the cat who had got the cream, or at least a handsome vet, and that even Lord Byron could see how happy I was.

At midnight, as Jake kissed me, Lord Byron did the polite thing and hopped off the sofa. The kiss ended up in the bedroom, and by now it was clear that Jake was staying the night.

'I'm glad I've won him round,' Jake said, as he slid under my duvet.

'Who?' I ask, feeling delirious as we cuddle up close.

'Your cat.'

I laugh, and kiss him again. 'Yes,' I say. 'So am I.'

Jake's hands start to navigate my body, reaching lower. Then he stops and his face recoils in horror.

'What is it?' I ask him.

'Er, nothing,' he says.

But I know exactly what it is, and peel back the duvet to find a purr-less Lord Byron lying between us, back to his old tricks.

'Oh, I thought . . .' Jake trails off, clearly relieved that he hasn't just pulled Chewbacca's sister.

'Yes,' I say. 'I know what you thought.' And I pick up Lord Byron and put him outside. Then I ignore his scratching against the door, as my lips devour the gorgeous man in my bed.

'You're a naughty girl, aren't you?' Jake's voice, between kisses. 'A naughty, naughty girl.'

'I can't help it,' I say, with a slight giggle. 'It's my nature.'

Alex Best is the author of *Loving George*.

36. THE OTHER WOMAN
Alex Best

I was pretty young the first time I fell in love. And quite innocent too. I didn't know about rules and how to play the game. It wouldn't have occurred to me to play hard to get.

I loved with all my heart and never so much as looked at another man. Jamie was a musician and would work late most nights. Not being much of a party animal myself, I'd prefer to take it easy and go to sleep early most nights. I think Jamie liked the fact that I kept the bed warm for him.

We were both very compatible and never a cross word was spoken between us. I didn't get jealous when I saw Jamie openly flirting with other females. After all, women would come and go but I was the one he chose to live with and I wasn't going anywhere.

I didn't mind that we never went out together. A home bird by nature, I was just as happy to curl up in front of the fire on a winter's evening. Anyway, I didn't even drink alcohol.

When Jamie's band finally got a record deal he was elated and danced around our bungalow for days on end. I was happy for him of course but hoped that fame wouldn't change him. Would our safe comfortable little existence be rocked by this recent news?

His album was met with unexpected success. It rocketed to number one and Jamie's manager wanted him to go on a world tour. It meant a lot of travelling on a tour bus and Jamie felt it would be best not to bring me along. I was sad of course. I knew I would miss him, but I couldn't begrudge him his dream.

When he packed his suitcase my heart was heavy. There was something very final about the way he zipped up his bags and snapped shut his guitar case. I didn't cry and tried not to let my emotions show. This was Jamie's destiny. After years of false starts and empty promises, his talents were finally going to be enjoyed by eager young fans all over the world from Germany to Japan.

The house was very lonely when he was gone. I missed the sound of Jamie singing in the shower every morning. At night, I slept on his side of the bed wondering when he was going to come home. Days turned into weeks and weeks turned into months. I hoped he wouldn't decide to stay in another country with a more pleasant climate.

I wasn't all alone of course. The housekeeper would come along twice a week, and Jamie's mother could pop in now and again to see how I was coping. The truth was, I wasn't coping at all well. The light had gone out of my life and I seemed to be existing rather than living. Jamie's mum was concerned that I was losing weight. She told me I needed to fatten up, but honestly it was no fun eating alone. Food held very little interest for me. I just wanted my man back.

I tried not to think about it too much, but sometimes I would worry about groupies. I'd heard Jamie and the lads discussing them now and again and these girls seemed to have very little morals. They'd hang around back stage waiting for the band. Jamie, as the lead singer, would have got more attention than the others. With his tousled blonde hair and chocolate brown eyes, I'm sure these brazen young women would find him irresistible. Suppose Jamie fell in love with a Spanish groupie and they decided to set up home on a sunny beach together? Suppose he forgot about me completely?

And then one day, while I was having a little cat nap by the kitchen Aga, I heard the sound of a car outside the house. I got up and stretching, I looked out the window. There was Jamie getting out of a taxi. He looked tanned and happy. I rushed to the door to meet him.

I'll never forget the shock that greeted me. Standing behind Jamie was a tall beautiful brunette with shiny dark hair. Jamie picked me up and hugged me before introducing us. He told me he'd like me to meet his future wife. I was devastated.

For the next few weeks I felt myself sink into a deep depression. Although the new woman tried to make friends, I still didn't like her. She had replaced me in Jamie's affections. I was no longer welcome to sleep on Jamie's bed.

The other woman bought me a bell, which I didn't like at all and ripped it off me. She seemed hurt but I didn't care. I wasn't that fickle and I couldn't be bought.

Months passed and I noticed the new woman was becoming fat. I couldn't understand it because she hardly ate anything. But then I found out she was expecting a baby. When I heard the news I ran away. I'd had enough.

Jamie found me in a neighbour's garden three days later. I was tired and hungry and fed up. He told me he had a present for me. I didn't care what the present was; I just wanted a good kip.

The present wasn't something to eat, nor something to

tie around my neck making me look foolish. It was a handsome furry cat called Danny. He had a mischievous look in his eye. I wanted to hate him. Only a few months ago, it had just been myself and Jamie. Now there was a new cat, another woman and a new baby on the way. What had I done to deserve all of this?

But love blossomed when I realised that Danny was very considerate, cuddly and quite attractive. We've become very close recently and I have to admit that love comes along when you least expect it. We even share a bed now.

We're all moving house soon. Jamie felt that our present house wouldn't be big enough for himself, the new woman, her baby, myself, Danny and our own imminent brood. Oh, did I forget to tell you? I'm due in six weeks. Before the other woman. Yes, I'm going to have kittens. Who would have ever thought it?